NORWICH SUBMER

Norwich Submerged

The meandering river and the Great Flood

Matthew Williams

Lasse Press

First published 2019
by the Lasse Press
2 St Giles Terrace, Norwich NR2 1NS, UK
www.lassepress.com
lassepress@gmail.com

ISBN-13: 978-1-9997752-5-4

Typeset in Garamond and Trade Gothic by
Curran Publishing Services Ltd, Norwich, UK

Manufactured in the UK by Cambrian Printers, Aberystwyth

Front cover illustration: incorporates images of Heigham Street (figures wading) and Devonshire Street
(laden cart). The former image is the view towards the city centre from a point midway between the
junctions with Old Palace Road and Barker Street.
Rear cover illustration: St Miles Bridge, viewed upstream in August 2018 and in August 1912.

One quarter of the author's royalties for this book are committed to the charity NORAH, Norfolk
Archives & Heritage Development Foundation. Further details at www.norah-df.org.uk

Contents

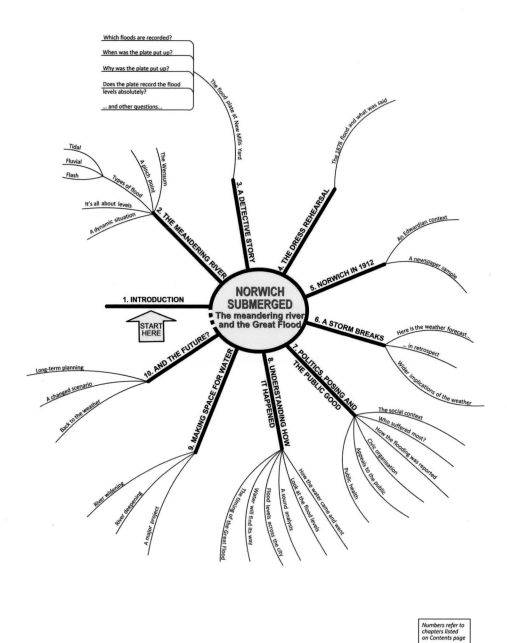

Figure 1 Branch diagram (or mind map) to show the structure of this book

The content within the mind map image includes:

Which floods are recorded?
When was the plate put up?
Why was the plate put up?
Does the plate record the flood levels absolutely?
... and other questions...

The flood plate at New Mills Yard

The 1878 flood and what was said

Tidal
Fluvial
Flash
Types of flood
A pinch point
The Wensum
It's all about levels
A dynamic situation

2. THE MEANDERING RIVER

3. A DETECTIVE STORY

4. THE DRESS REHEARSAL

5. NORWICH IN 1912
An Edwardian context
A newspaper sample

NORWICH SUBMERGED
The meandering river and the Great Flood

1. INTRODUCTION
START HERE

6. A STORM BREAKS
Here is the weather forecast...
... in retrospect
Wider implications of the weather

7. POLITICS, POSING AND THE PUBLIC GOOD
The social context
Who suffered most?
How the flooding was reported
Civic organisation
Appeals to the public
Public health

8. UNDERSTANDING HOW IT HAPPENED
How the water came and went
Look at the flood levels
A sound analysis
Flood levels across the city
Water will find its way
The timing of the Great Flood

9. MAKING SPACE FOR WATER
River widening
River deepening
A major project

10. AND THE FUTURE?
Long-term planning
A changed scenario
Back to the weather

Numbers refer to chapters listed on Contents page

Illustrations

For ease of reference, a map of the central Norwich area is at the back of this book (as Appendix 6) on which is marked the approximate locations of photographic and other numbered figures appearing throughout the book.

Boxes

Foreword

The River Wensum flows gently, languidly through the heart of Norwich and for a short stretch between the Jarrold and Bishop's Bridge retains an almost rural quality. For centuries it was a vital part of the city's economy, a busy commercial highway providing water for households' drinking and washing, for dyers, for fellmongers and a means for clearing both commercial and domestic effluent.

Now there are plans to enhance the recreational value of the river within the city – but let us not forget occasionally the Wensum has become a raging torrent bursting its banks, disrupting trade, flooding homes and business premises, and causing hardship for the citizens and problems for the city's government.

Much has been written about the social effect of the floods, of livestock lost, of property and livelihoods destroyed, of the financial cost and of subsequent preventive measures put in place. There can now be no personal memories of either 1878 or 1912, the two most recent floods, but photography has seared both into our realisation of the effect they had on Norwich. Photographs freeze the moment, and along with stories of individual acts of bravery enable us mentally to contain the inexorable force of nature, and confront us with the elemental power of water.

In *Norwich Submerged* Matthew Williams has taken a new approach: he has analysed the river itself, its passage from its source, the twists and turns it takes until it reaches the city, its nature within the city boundaries, its tributaries and its joining with the Yare for its eventual passage to the sea.

The reason why floods have occurred becomes clearer. Agricultural change, narrowing both natural and human-made, weather conditions and the seasons of the year have all enhanced both the effect and likelihood of serious flooding. Most cogent to our generation, with the ongoing debate about climate change, Matthew poses the question: could such flooding happen again?

Norwich Submerged is a diligent, thought-provoking study of all aspects of our river, the Wensum and its tributaries. It remains for the reader to construe the social and economic effect another flood like 1878 or 1912 would have on both the city and its people and the rural hinterland.

Surely the challenge for the citizens of both Norwich and of Norfolk is not to fall into a false sense of security but to stay alert and continue to impress upon both local and national government the need for measures to be put in place so, as far as is humanly possible, future flooding can be prevented rather than waiting to deal with the devastating and expensive aftermath of another inundation.

Barbara Miller MBE
Norwich Blue Badge Guide

Acknowledgements

It bodes well for Norwich that so many individuals, both locally and beyond, are actively involved in increasing the pool of knowledge about the city's history, a healthy process if we are to continue to inform decisions about its future. There is a noticeable willingness among those who live here to assist in projects such as the one behind this book. The consequence is that in trying to put together a comprehensive list of names to thank, there is a danger of inadvertently leaving someone out.

I would however like specifically to acknowledge the assistance and encouragement given to me by Brian Ayers, Terry Burkill, Stephen Burt, Rosemary Dixon, Clare Everitt, Karl Field, Andrew Fisher, Derek James, Mike Kendon, Ros Lewis, David Paddick, Jonathan Plunkett, Irina Sargeant, Gary Tuson and the late David Cubitt. I am grateful to the members of staff at Norfolk Record Office and Norfolk Heritage Centre who went out of their way to offer advice and information, as did employees of Environment Agency and ATB Laurence Scott. I would also have struggled without the generous assistance of friends and strangers during the patient process of surveying flood plates.

In turning the study into a book, I need to express appreciation for organisations and individuals who have generously allowed use of illustrations (as listed on pages 100–102). I am honoured that Barbara Miller was prepared to write my foreword. I also want to acknowledge the painstaking guidance given by Susan Curran, the support from my wife Amanda, and the vital work of proofreaders Paul Simmonds and Meg Norman.

Any errors or omissions remain my responsibility, and will of course be corrected when the opportunity arises.

Matthew Williams

Figure 2 Flooding in Heigham Street, 1912

1 Introduction

For more than a century 1912 has been remembered by the world as the year the *Titanic* went down in the North Atlantic. The people of Norwich also have reason to recall it as the year of the Great Flood, the worst inundation known to have affected the city and the surrounding area. There is of course no longer anyone alive who has a direct memory of this event, but its legacy remains with us today, if only in the form of the metal flood plates that can still be seen on Norwich river walls if you look over the bridge parapets.

I should perhaps qualify that statement of the 'worst inundation' by adding the words 'to date', recognising that the label 'Great' should be reserved for absolutely the most severe of such happenings. For 30 or so years prior to 1912, the Great Flood was used to refer to the one of 1878, a deluge of only slightly lesser magnitude than the one 34 years later. The twentieth-century Great Flood nevertheless earned the right to the title, and has held onto it for over 100 years. Whether another flood will one day supersede it can only remain to be seen.

The Great Flood was by no means confined to the city's boundaries, and caused long-lasting damage over a wide part of Norfolk – not least through the destruction of many bridges, the loss of fields of crops and the permanent end of the Aylsham navigation.[1]

---

1 This was the 18 km long canal route along the Bure valley to Aylsham, opened in 1779.

However, parts of the built-up area of Norwich were extremely hard-hit, and this book concerns itself primarily with the urban area.

The same downpour that led to flooding was also a factor in triggering localised incidents of subsidence on higher ground in the city. While such events are interesting, I have not covered them here as they are not directly related to the rise in river level. The focus is firmly on the lower-lying areas that were submerged.

Norwich has long suffered intermittent floods. In his writings about Norwich in the early 1800s,[2] the geologist William Smith (Figure 3) made reference to an inundation of 1762 which had 'deluged 300 houses and 8 churches', and he commented that 'it would be curious to investigate the causes of such extraordinary floods'.

Smith did himself do some work towards such an investigation,[3] and he went on to make speculative comments on possible causes of the floods. While he did not have the benefit of the accurate survey data, photographic and other information that became available following the subsequent 'great' floods of 1878 and 1912, it was evident to him as both a geologist and a surveyor that Norwich was always going to be affected by flooding.

The purpose of this book is to do exactly what William Smith's curiosity suggested – to tease out the reasons why. An investigation of this kind may put us in a better position to judge whether we should expect another Great Flood.

Figure 3 Portrait of William Smith, dated 1837

You will find accounts of the 1912 flood on various websites and online forums, and many of these draw heavily on the widely circulated *Illustrated Record of the Great Flood*, which was published shortly after the event (Figure 4) and contained a selection of dramatic photographs interspersed with anecdotal text.[4] In commencing this project it was an obvious starting point for me to read again through this document as a key contemporary source of information.

The *Illustrated Record* uses a florid style of writing which seems strong on adjectives but less clear on chronology or hard facts. The same is true of the captions to the photographs which back up the text. My impression is that this semi-official account may have been

---

2   Undated, untitled work held in the Oxford University Museum of Natural History Archives and Library Collection, WS/F/4/3/001.
3   For example, his diary records that he was in Norwich surveying the river bank levels at Heigham on 25–26 July 1805.
4   City of Norwich. 1912. *Illustrated Record of the Great Flood of August 1912*. Roberts & Co. There was a similar contemporary small book published by A. E. Coe & Son titled *Photographs of the Floods in Norwich and Norfolk*, August 1912.

written more to satisfy morale-boosting or fundraising objectives than to provide a dispassionate account of what had happened in physical terms.

Rather than rework an emotive tale of human disaster and heroic deeds,[5] I want to get a deeper understanding of why and how the flooding occurred, one based on a rational 'model' for the lie of the land in the river-affected areas. This is a similar approach to the one I used in *Subterranean Norwich: the grain of the city*, which among other things encourages an understanding of absolute vertical elevations – allowing us to compare relative heights of land and water. While that book refers along the way to both water levels and floods in connection with underground conditions, I felt it was worth delving into this subject in greater detail as the river is so central to the city. In fact it is integral to why Norwich was first founded in its particular location.

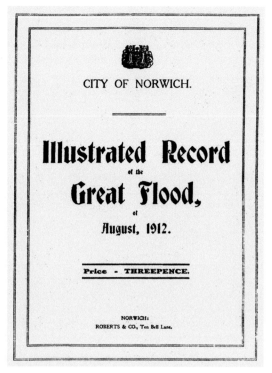

Figure 4 Cover of the earliest official account of the 1912 flood

The model for the 1912 flood being explored here is informed by some newly acquired observations and measurements, coupled with a search through contemporary newspaper reports and some less well-known accounts of the time. I spent many hours leafing through pages of City Council minutes, and while I did not always find what I was after (for example, frustratingly there was nothing about the putting-up of the flood plates), there did emerge much useful information on the subject to corroborate or correct other accounts I had read.

I have also worked out a way of extracting useful technical information (in particular water levels) from the many contemporary photographs that we have of the flood, beyond their value as a somewhat repetitive catalogue of views of watery streets and stoical residents.

The aim of the account presented here is to provide a factual context for the interpretation of descriptions and images of the time and for critical assessment of more recent accounts of that event and other floods. It might also help to offer a few insights into

---

5   There is a comprehensive modern account in Neil Storey's book *Norfolk Floods*, published on the centenary of the 1912 flood.

the social context of the early twentieth century. My intention is that the approach and material in this book will be a relevant contribution to the consideration of the fluvial flood risk to Norwich, both now and in the years ahead, not least in the light of the recently published *River Wensum Strategy* which seeks to preserve and enhance Norwich's river for the benefit of the city.[6]

If you know the city and appreciate its rich heritage, I hope you find interest here and something to enhance your understanding of Norwich as a physical entity.

Metric and imperial units

Much of the original information in 1912 was recorded in imperial units of feet, inches, acres and gallons. Where it is appropriate to the historic source, these units have been quoted in the text, usually with a conversion to metric units of metres, centimetres, hectares and litres in brackets. Where modern interpretation or commentary is being made, I have used metric units by default, but added the imperial units in brackets where this is useful for comparison. I have sought to avoid irritating readers with obsessive dual representation of figures, but if approximate conversions of units are needed, the following should suffice:

| 1 foot = 0.305 metre | 1 acre = 0.4 hectare | 1 gallon = 4.5 litres |
| 1 metre = 3.3 feet | 1 hectare = 2.5 acres | 1 litre = 0.22 gallons |

6   River Wensum Strategic Partnership. 2018. *River Wensum Strategy*. Norwich City Council.

Figure 5 Multiple meanders are shown well today by the Upper Wensum at Lenwade, viewed from Marriott's Way

2 The meandering river

The Wensum

The name of the river passing through Norwich is thought to derive from an Old English word meaning 'winding'. Although most rivers do meander,[1] a glance at a map (for example Figure 57) will show you the word is especially appropriate for the Wensum. This sinuosity (Figure 5) is evident over much of the river's generally eastward-flowing course, although its natural line has in places been straightened artificially over historical time.

In geographical terms, the River Wensum is a relatively 'mature' river, which means it has largely ceased eroding downwards into the landscape. In its natural condition it exists as a typically broad, slow-moving channel (in contrast with a youthful fast-flowing stream) and carries a relatively large volume of water collected from its various tributaries farther upstream. There is nevertheless a certain amount of attrition (erosion) still going on, chiefly on the outside of the river bends, especially when the water level is high, as well as the accumulation of sand and mud (deposition) on the inside of the meanders at quieter times.

Without interference, the river's course naturally switches from side to side along

---

1   The word 'meander' itself comes from the name of a river in Turkey.

its course within its marshy flood plain. In the Wensum's case, this has reached some 500 metres in width by the time the river crosses the outer ring road and enters the city limits at Sweetbriar Road.

Once within the built-up area, the river continues to wind, but we start to lose sight of the original natural flood plain. This is because the originally low-lying land has in many places over the centuries been 'reclaimed' to usefulness by filling, raising and the process of development. Indeed, much of this raised ground is now capped by buildings, some still incorporating elements of what were originally warehouses, malt houses and factories deliberately positioned within close reach of the river, either for water supply or for access to river quay facilities. A good example of such filling and riverside development is the stretch below New Mills (see the geological cross-section in Figure 6).

The natural river channel, which in some places had in former centuries been 'braided' or split into multiple channels, has become tamed and formalised by human effort, straightened and 'canalised' between hard vertical banks. Over the years there had been a tendency for the channel progressively to be narrowed as a result of replacement river walls or quay headings repeatedly being built in front of the previous ones.

A pinch point

The shape of the natural landscape is a contributing reason for the disappearing flood plain in Norwich. This is because the river has to find its way between what are now two areas of higher ground, centred respectively on the marketplace area and Mousehold Heath. This lack of elbow room had the effect of halving the width of the original flood plain along the course of the river through the city centre to barely 200 metres in places.

It is the natural topography that has dictated the need for a dramatic 120 degree rightward bend in the river's course around the back of what is now the Cathedral Close area and past Cow Tower. Having made this turn, the river's left edge nibbles at the rising slope of Thorpe Hamlet before it runs southwards past the railway station on towards the football ground. Once there, the Wensum swings left again, its right edge now grinding against the rising ground of Bracondale, eventually to resume its generally eastward course towards Great Yarmouth. On leaving the city in the Whitlingham area, the flood plain broadens out again to a more relaxed 500 metres, and the meandering channel itself is made wider by the injection of additional flow from another tributary (the Yare) which joins it at Trowse Eye, having itself skirted the south side of the city.

It is that pinching of the flood plain over its course a few hundred metres upstream and downstream from the Cow Tower bend that made these attractive points for early human travellers to wade across the river, in turn dictating the alignment of the approaching thoroughfares – one running north–south, fording in what is now the Fye Bridge area, and the other east–west at the location of what became Bishop Bridge. It is no surprise that the main original settlement centred around the crossroad of these two straight routes, in what we know as Tombland.

The underlying geological reasons for the existence of the higher ground that apparently deflects the route of the Wensum through the city centre are not fully understood, but it is thought there were several factors in play. It is necessary to explain some potentially large changes over recent geological time in the relationship between the level of the

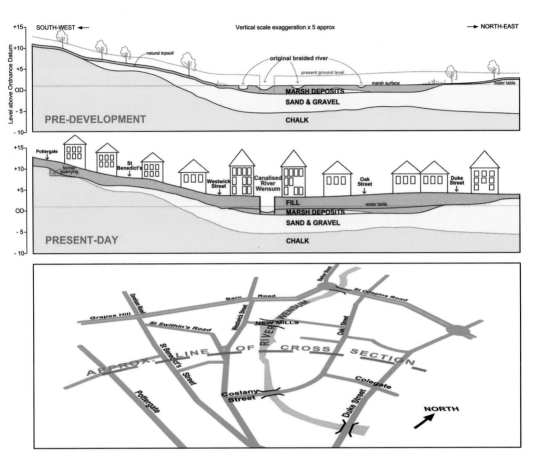

Figure 6 Diagrammatic cross-section of the Wensum valley at a point shortly after it has entered the city centre, showing the natural flood plain and later development

land surface and the base level down to which the river is trying to erode. Nowadays the level of the river on the lower side of New Mills is more or less the same as sea level, but at various stages in the past the level of the sea would temporarily have been considerably lower than it is now,[2] which would be expected to rejuvenate the process of downward river erosion.

More intriguing is the suggestion that the solid landmass in the Norwich area may have risen over time (owing to deep structural buoyancy effects known as isostasy), so that the meandering river became more deeply cut into the landscape than it was originally. This process of incision could help to explain the height and steepness (at least by Norfolk standards) of the valley sides at Thorpe Hamlet and above King Street, which exceed 45 m and 30 m in elevation respectively.

Geologists tell us the landscape as we know it evolved as the result of two main periods

2   This occurred during extended cold periods when the ice caps were larger.

of activity: a deep glaciation about 450,000 years ago, involving substantial erosion and deposition of thick gravels and clays, then a series of more recent but less intensive cold periods during the last 130-300,000 years, which gradually modified the landscape by processes of freezing and thawing, soil creep and the cutting of the valley features we see today.[3] After that time, conditions moderated and settled, with forests and marshland becoming established. They were of course cleared in time, and the shape of the river today is strongly influenced by human activities.

Types of flood

At this point it will be useful to flag up a few broad definitions and to distinguish the main types of flood.

So far as we can tell, the historically recorded flood events affecting Norwich were predominantly of the fluvial type, because they usually followed very heavy or extensive

Tidal flooding

This is essentially the same thing as coastal inundation, because it is caused by an exceptionally high sea level, usually resulting from the combination of high tides and weather conditions, such as occurred in February 1953. A tidal surge up the river system can also affect areas a long way inland, which potentially include Norwich because it is at the head of the Yare estuary.

Fluvial flooding

This is the result of an excessive volume of water moving down the river system as the result of heavy and/or prolonged rainfall or a thaw after snowfall. In the past this was sometimes referred to as a freshet. It is often combined with the more immediate effect of partial blockage of watercourses by vegetation or debris which can lead to the overtopping of river banks. A long period of wet weather can also lead to a progressive rise in the groundwater level, which can lead to chronic flooding over a longer timescale than that triggered by a surge in river level alone.

Flash flooding

This type of flooding (sometimes known as pluvial flooding) is mainly attributable to human factors, and has become an increasingly frequent modern phenomenon during storms that affect built-up areas. The key contributory cause is the replacement of the natural absorbent surface layers of topsoil or vegetation by artificial impermeable surfaces such as paving or the sealed roofs of buildings. It is an inevitable consequence of development of any previously rural locality as a city expands. During heavy precipitation hard surfaces rapidly displace rainwater sideways down-gradient, either by flow over the surface or via piped drainage systems, to some point downslope where the water cannot get away fast enough, causing temporary flooding.

---

3 The first period was known as the Anglian Glaciation; notable among the later events was the Wollstonian Glaciation.

Figure 7 New Mills, viewed from the lower (tidal) side

rainfall. However, some of the descriptions we have suggest a contribution of other types of causal factors, such as tidal influence – which can for example fill the flood plains downstream of the city with water and reduce the rate at which fluvial floodwater can drain away.

Most late twentieth and twenty-first century reports of flooding within the city involve a large element of flash flooding, which could be considered a failure of design, or could equally be argued is the consequence of overdevelopment of a locality.

It is worth making this distinction between flood types as it helps us to recognise why Norwich has a long history of flooding: it is closely related to its position at the head of navigation on the River Yare/Wensum system.

The geographical significance of the head of navigation in Norwich's case is that it shows us where the estuary begins. All of the river eastwards (in other words, downstream) from New Mills is tidal (Figure 7), with little if any natural fall in absolute water level all the way from Norwich to the sea, a distance of some 50 km as the river flows. That's why when the tide arrives twice each day, the river level in the city centre is temporarily a little higher, leaving a wet mark up the river wall after it has fallen again. During high tide, the lowest-lying drainage outfalls are unable to discharge water by gravity into the Wensum until the river level has fallen again, and some of them are fitted with flaps to stop the tidal water flowing back up the sewer.

As you might expect, the flow and the amount of water in the watercourse increase along its course, and as the river gets pinched on its way through the city centre it tends to increase in depth rather than width, before eventually widening out again. The stretch between Hellesdon and New Mills included several locations where there were probably ancient fording points: but by about 2 km downstream from New Mills the Wensum is probably a little too deep to wade across with comfort.

On the other hand, if you are sailing up the river from the sea, Norwich is as far as you can get before the river level starts stepping up via a series of weirs. The first is that at New Mills, which is located on the west side of the city centre off Barn Road. The first mill known to have been here was constructed in 1430, although it almost certainly replaced earlier mills. At this point you have to moor your boat and transfer to a canoe, then paddle farther upstream against the flow. A weir is of necessity a partial constriction of the river, intended to raise the water level on its upstream side. This inevitably increases the risk of water overtopping the banks unless those banks are deliberately raised.

In archaeological terms, it is these twin factors – the head of navigation and the lowest fording point – that help to explain why historic settlements were established around this point, and later grew into a city.

In time, the fording points became raised as causeways, then bridges were built well clear of the flowing water. As a further consequence, the processes of urbanisation led to the channelling of the river course and the raising of the banks, constricting the water flow and depriving the river of its natural flood plains. These predominantly ground-raising processes are described in *Subterranean Norwich: the grain of the city*, and they are of course by no means unique to this particular city.

It's all about levels

On the basis that water does not flow uphill, being able to think in levels is an important tool in understanding both the shape of the landscape and the drainage conditions in Norwich, or anywhere else for that matter. To get the most out of this book you need to understand the concept of 'relative levels', so here is a brief explanation for those who need it.

The Ordnance Datum (abbreviated to OD) is an arbitrary horizontal line set by the Ordnance Survey – they chose to fix it on the a measurement of mean sea level at Newlyn in Cornwall.[3] All ground levels (and other recorded heights or depths) can be measured and expressed absolutely in relation to this imaginary datum line, the position of which can relatively easily be determined by reference to local Ordnance

Figure 8 An Ordnance Survey bench mark, on St Margaret's Church between St Benedict's and Westwick Street, with a value of +6.72m AOD.

---

3 Prior to the 1920s, the datum was fixed at Liverpool, but this was changed to Newlyn during a more accurate national re-survey carried out between 1912 and 1921.

Figure 9 Measuring relative levels

Survey bench marks. These marks are short horizontal lines chiselled onto various fixed objects dotted around across the country (Figure 8), with their height above OD (i.e. above the zero line) recorded on Ordnance Survey maps.[4]

I explained at some length in *Subterranean Norwich* why it is more fundamentally useful to think of the position of some underground layer in terms of its level (in relation to similar layers elsewhere) than to just record its depth below the present ground surface. The ground surface is not reliable as a consistent measuring point because it goes up and down across the city, and may also change over a period of time. Absolute levels are usually expressed as metres above or below OD.

A simple builder's level (a horizontally mounted telescope: see Figure 9), a calibrated staff (marked off in centimetres) and a notebook are all that are needed to be able to measure the OD level of any feature if there is a nearby Ordnance Survey bench mark to work from.

If you imagine being able to view Norwich horizontally from a great distance, you could in theory mark a scale of metres up the side of your view, with zero on the scale set a couple of metres beneath the lowest ground in the city centre (probably near Bishopgate) and the scale extending upward sufficiently to measure off the relative level of the top of the Cathedral spire, which is actually at about 102 m above our zero line, in other words at +102 m AOD (above Ordnance Datum). The spire is actually 96 m high, but that is the height when measured from the ground surface in The Close, which is itself at about +6 m AOD. (If you can understand that calculation, you have the concept of levels.)

Using a similar method we can determine the relative levels of other points of interest

---

4 These days, other surveying techniques (based on satellite measuring) are used, but there is still a good legacy of visible bench marks left from a hundred years of activity by Ordnance Survey.

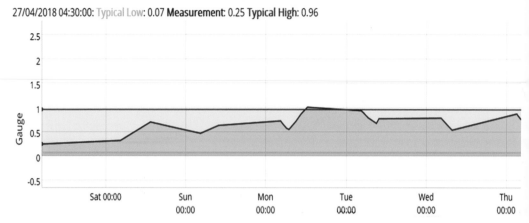

Figure 10 Typical automated river level plot (metres AOD) for the lower side of New Mills, for the week following 27 April 2018

in the landscape, such as the top of the castle mound (at around +33 m AOD), the floor level of The Forum (around +26 m AOD) or the level of the football pitch at Carrow Road (little more than +3 m AOD).

So much for the land surface; in this book we shall be making extensive use of relative levels when describing the height of temporary floodwater. At normal times, the water level in the River Wensum on the lower side of New Mills is at or slightly below +1 m AOD (see Figure 10), so we could imagine constructing a permanent scale at the edge of the river with its zero mark planted somewhere in the river bed, and its 1 m mark usually visible just above the water level.[5]

During times of flood, the river is capable of rising to well above +1 m AOD, so it would be as well if our scale were at least 5 m high so we can at any time read off the river water level directly in terms of metres AOD. Being able to quantify and interpret these absolute flood levels in terms of OD is a most useful way of understanding what happens, and we will be making use of these levels in later chapters.

A dynamic situation

Another important point to recognise is that the River Wensum, as with any river, is not a static entity but a constantly changing system. It only exists because of a constant equilibrium between the amount of water continually flowing in at the upstream end and that flowing out downstream.

The relative balance between these two rates of flow over a given period of time, measured at any two appropriate points such as upstream and downstream of the city, dictates whether the water level between those two points remains the same, or whether it is rising or falling.[6] The water itself is always on the move, just passing through the system.

---

5   Such scales marked up as metres AOD do still exist in places where the river level needs to be monitored and controlled (see Figure 11), but these days the reading of water levels is automated.

Figure 11 River level gauges are usually marked in tenths of a metre AOD. The one on the left is at Costessey Mill, on the River Wensum 7 km upstream from New Mills, which is showing a water level of +5.4 m AOD. On the right is the gauge on the upstream side of New Mills in the city centre, reading +2.5 m AOD (the line visible immediately above the 9 is the +3.0 m mark).

Hour by hour, the water level downstream from New Mills usually fluctuates over a range of a fraction of a metre because of the influence of the twice-daily tide, and this can be further complicated by short-term variations in the volume of water being allowed to flow over the New Mills weir as a result of mechanical adjustments to the sluice level (apparent on the plot in Figure 10).[7] If the sluice is raised a little, proportionately more water is held back by the weir, and the difference in water level between the upstream and downstream sides (known as the head) increases (see Figure 12).

We have already noted how most of the historical floods that have periodically affected Norwich are of the fluvial type. In other words, when considering that part of the River Wensum running through the city, for a time the rate of inflow considerably exceeded the rate of outflow, with the result that the river level rose to a higher level than its normal state. Precisely to what height it rose is something we will be exploring in detail in Chapter 8, and we can use water levels rather than merely water depths.

---

6 In doing this calculation, we must of course allow for any additional water entering the river via side-drains or tributaries between our two monitoring points.

7 At New Mills there are actually five parallel sluice channels, two of which are normally used to control the river level upstream and downstream, taking into account the tide level and based on monitoring every 15 minutes. The other sluices can also be dropped in the event of a storm. In recent years the automated system has typically been set to hold the upper water level at +2.44 m AOD. There is a proposal to install an electricity-generating turbine in one of the sluices on the upstream side of the building.

Figure 12 The upstream side of New Mills, where water level is monitored. The chain is to catch canoeists and perhaps also large items of floating debris.

Figure 13 The junction of New Mills Yard with Westwick Street

3 A detective story

The flood plate at New Mills Yard

A good place to start our exploration of flooding in Norwich is the steel marker plate attached to a wall at New Mills Yard (Figure 13).[1] It is so far as I know the only one of its kind in the city, and it is worth taking a closer look (Figure 14, overleaf).

The plate provides an overview of the impact of historic floods, since it purports to record the highest level up the wall reached by floodwater during all of the worst such events. The recorded years that are visible range from 1570 through to 1912, with that latest one the highest. However, look very closely and you will see at least one date is almost hidden from view by the tarmac that has been placed against the wall.

The flood plate answers our initial questions about historic flood levels, but it raises others, as we shall see. Providing satisfactory answers to some of these is something of a detective story.

---

1 This starting point is just a few metres away from a location where John Crome set up his easel to paint *New Mills: Men Wading*, the picture used as the starting point in *Subterranean Norwich*.

15

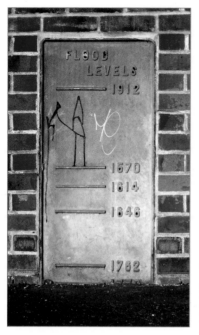

Figure 14 The marker plate at New Mills Yard

Which floods are recorded?

The eight flood events recorded on the steel plate, arranged in order of height and including the three dates covered at its base, are:

1912
1570
1614
1646
1762
1770
1734
1878

When was the plate put up?

The plate seems to have been put in place shortly after 1912, replacing an earlier steel plate which had been inscribed with lines showing water levels. The earlier plate had been mounted immediately to the right-hand side of a more ancient stone set in the wall, inscribed with lines showing water levels of five (in other words, not all) of the earlier floods (Figure 15).[2] The replacement plate remained alongside the original flood stone for seven decades until the wall was demolished, and the steel plate was subsequently re-erected on the boundary wall that is there today.

Why was the plate put up?

It may reasonably be assumed this surviving steel plate was created because the original stone and adjacent metal versions were not sufficiently tall to accommodate the 1912 level. Indeed, there exists an archive photograph (and also a piece of early film footage[3]) showing a similar but shorter plate on the same piece of wall with the new flood level freshly chalked above it (Figure 17).[4] This is the basis for saying that the surviving plate was a replacement of this previous steel plate. There are minor differences in the lettering which suggest that an altogether new plate was indeed cast, rather than it being a

---

2 That stone was not in fact the only one in this part of Norwich: there was at one time a similar stone set in the wall of New Brewery Yard, less than 40 m away, with lines inscribed recording the 1762, 1770 and 1878 flood levels. That stone was photographed with the 1912 flood level chalked above it (see Figure 16), interestingly with the spacing of individual flood lines not quite matching those on the New Mills Yard plate despite its close proximity.

3 Viewable on the British Film Institute website.

4 The brickwork can be matched to that of the original New Mills wall, although the Picture Norfolk record archive erroneously gives the location as Bullard's Brewery.

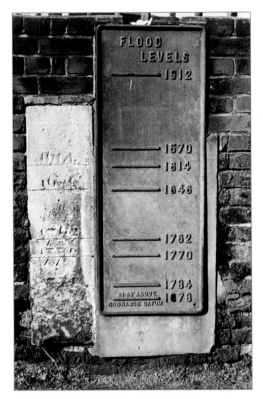

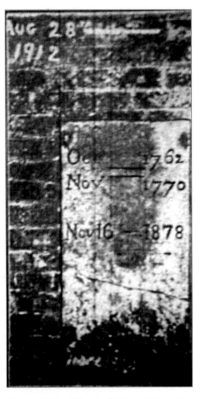

Figure 15 New Mills flood marker plate, pictured in the 1960s when the original stone marker was still in place

Figure 16 A different flood marker, now lost, originally at New Brewery Yard, with a chalk line added above to show the 1912 level

Figure 17 The original New Mills marker plate, with a ghostly hand indicating the 1912 flood level

Figure 18
Level information visible on the New Mills marker plate in 1961

modification of the original. Perhaps the first steel plate was put up next to the old flood stone because the latter was eroding away, but there is evidence to suggest this was done only a short time prior to 1912.[5]

Does the plate record the flood levels absolutely?

Archive photographs taken before 1986 (Figure 18) show that the lowest line on the steel plate (recording the flood level of 1878) is annotated with a level expressed in feet above OD. That information is not visible today because it is now hidden beneath the path level: however, from these earlier photographs the figure appears to read 13.66 ft AOD.

Is the flood plate still on its original wall?

Quite evidently not: the flood plate at New Mills Yard is now mounted on a modern (late 1980s) brick boundary wall. The original eroded stone marker, an integral part of the demolished wall, could evidently not be retained. This raises some further specific questions which we will seek to answer.

So if the steel plate has been re-mounted, can we be confident it has been put back in a similar position and at the same level?

A newspaper cutting dated 14 March 1986[6] showing the wall about to be demolished (Figure 19) makes it clear the builders were indeed aware of the need to put the plate back at the correct level, which is at least encouraging. An accompanying photograph also shows its original position close to the Westwick Street junction to be very similar to today's, close to a Royal Mail postbox.

As part of this study, I used the simple surveying method described in Chapter 1 to determine the absolute level of the 1912 flood line shown on the plate in its present position. I also compared the position of this line with another 1912 plate nearby, a dedicated marker in its original position on the eastern corner of the New Mills Pumping Station building about 60 m to the north-east (Figure 20). Measurement confirms that

---

5   It is almost certainly the plate referred to as 'recently produced' in the *Illustrated Record of the Great Flood of August 1912*, page 16. And H. B. Woodward's *Geological Memoir* of 1881 refers only to the flood stone, so the steel plate certainly did not exist at that earlier date.

6   In George Plunkett's scrapbook, provided by Jonathan Plunkett, private correspondence.

Figure 19 Newspaper article from March 1986 featuring the plate about to be moved

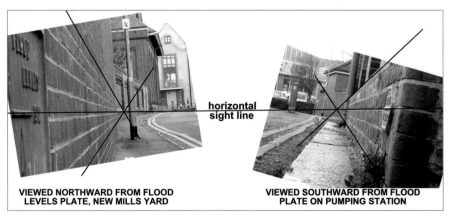

Figure 20 Sighting drawing to show that the two 1912 flood levels recorded at New Mills Yard are identical. The photographs from each direction have been rotated so as to sight along the horizontal brick course at the height of the flood mark, and lines of perspective drawn along higher and lower brick courses to intersect at a 'vanishing point' which is a horizontal horizon passing through both flood marks.

the two lines are at an identical level of +4.01 m AOD. From this exercise it can safely be concluded that the level of the larger plate was not permanently changed at the time of its moving, as it still matches that of the nearby plate which we can assume has not been disturbed.

Why then has the plate the appearance that it has slid down the wall, with its lower part (about 270 mm) now hidden below the ground surface?

Given the answer to the previous question, the only possible explanation is that the ground level has been substantially raised since the original plate was fixed, burying its lower portion. This probably occurred during the late 1980s redevelopment which involved extensive reconstruction of the Westwick Street area and a general raising of the road level. If that is the case, then it seems likely that some nearby granite setts recently exposed beneath the roadway tarmac (Figure 21) must have been relaid at the new higher road level.

Is the level above OD of the 1878 flood (as marked on the plate) recorded correctly?

This is a slightly complicated question. It is not essential for you to follow in detail the paragraphs that follow, but if you are at all mathematically minded you may be interested in this part of the detective story.

When the inferred position of the 1878 line (labelled '13.66 ft above Ordnance Datum') is measured using standard surveying methods using local bench marks, it is be found to be at about +3.1 m AOD, or about a metre lower than the label indicates (13.66 ft is actually 4.16 m). Therefore the simple answer is 'no'.

However, a relevant fact to note here is that there occurred a major recalibration and re-measurement of Ordnance Survey bench marks in the 1920s, such that their value recorded on OS maps in this area of Norwich reduced by some 1.0–1.5 ft (0.3–0.5 m).[7] But that is not sufficient to explain the difference in this case, so the plot thickens.

The contemporary *Illustrated Record of the Great Flood,* produced with the collaboration

Figure 21 Granite setts exposed in New Mills Yard, February 2018

---

7   For example, a nearby OS bench mark on the corner of Lothian Street and Barn Road is shown on the 1907 map (visible in Figure 55) as having the value 19.5 ft above OD, and the very same bench mark on the 1928 map is shown as 18.2 ft.

Biggest Flood ever Recorded in Norwich.

Mr. Collins has supplied figures giving the height to which the principal floods of the last three hundred years reached, viz :—

1614	... 15ft. 6½ins. above mean high water.				
1646	... 15ft. 3ins.	,,	,,	,,	,,
1734	... 13ft. 10½ins.	,,	,,	,,	,,
1762	... 14ft. 6½ins.	,,	,,	,,	,,
1770	.. 14ft. 3½ins.	,,	,,	,,	,,
1878	... 13ft. 8ins.	,,	,,	,,	,,
1912	... 16ft. 6½ins.	,,	,,	,,	,,

of the City Council, on its last page lists the various flood levels at New Mills as numerical heights 'above mean high water' (Figure 22). That for 1878 is given as 13 ft 8 in, or in decimal, 13.66 ft. Coincidence?

Now 'mean high water' is not the same as OD, but is a tidal measurement which in the Yare catchment is expressed in relation to Yarmouth Bar. That particular datum is 0.99 m below the modern zero OD. That 13 ft 8 in translates to 13.66 ft is probably more than coincidence, and we may conclude that the 1878 line does seem to be at the correct level, except that it has been erroneously labelled 'above Ordnance Datum' instead of 'above mean high water'.

To check this, we can convert the 1912 flood level, quoted in print as 16 ft 6½ ins, to metres, then in turn reduce it by 0.99, to give a value (in metres AOD) of +4.05 m AOD, which is very close to the level of the flood plate I have measured directly as part of this study.

In summary, is a reasonable conclusion that the lines marked on the repositioned flood plate at New Mills Yard do correctly record the levels at which the water was lapping there during the listed flood events.

As a postscript, during the preparation of this book the old flood stone was found lying on the floor at New Mills pumping station, where it has probably been stored since 1986. Although highly weathered, it would make a nice exhibit somewhere, but is probably best not displayed vertically, unless it can be fixed at precisely the correct level: we would not wish to create any future confusion!

I hope we have cleared up any lingering uncertainty about interpretation of the levels shown on the flood plate, and now we can move on to consider in more detail how the flooding happened in the New Mills area and elsewhere in the city.

Figure 23 Magic lantern view of flooded Napier Street
in 1878

4 The dress rehearsal

The 1878 flood and what was said

I have already mentioned that the flooding that affected the city in 1878 was often referred to as the 'Great Flood' for the three decades that followed, until it was superseded by the greater 1912 flood.

You may have noticed that the water levels recorded on our flood plate for six floods in previous centuries were in fact higher than the level measured during the 1878 'Great Flood'. This could be because the consequences of this flood were a greater issue than merely the height the water reached. Perhaps the perceived disruption in those earlier times, while serious, was of less lasting significance, because of lower population density, and perhaps also because intermittent flooding of low-lying areas was more accepted as a fact of life than in the slightly more genteel times of the late nineteenth century.

Useful descriptive information on the flood, which occurred in the middle of November 1878, is available from newspapers of the time. These included reports published from 18 to 30 November in the *Norwich Mercury*, the *Eastern Daily Press*, supplements to the *Norfolk Chronicle and Norwich Gazette*, and the *Norwich Argus*. For example, the *Norwich Mercury* of 20 November reported:

DISASTROUS FLOODS IN NORWICH AND NORFOLK – GREAT
DAMAGE TO PROPERTY – THOUSANDS OF PEOPLE
TEMPORARILY HOMELESS – GREAT DISTRESS PREVAILING

For the first time in upwards of a century Norwich has been visited by a calamity
such as has often occurred in other parts of the country, but which here was totally
unexpected. … though the utmost anxiety was felt by those who watched the
rain gauges, yet it was never for a moment anticipated that the waters would have
gathered in such an immense body as has, unfortunately, been the case.

Beyond the contemporary press reports, a sound source of information is Horace B.
Woodward's *Memoir of the Geological Survey covering the Country around Norwich*,
published in 1881 to accompany the first official geological survey map. He supplemented
his account of the physical geography of the area with a comprehensive chronological
list of all the floods that had affected
Norfolk since AD 575, based on named
documentary sources, He listed 30 in
total, explicitly referencing which ones
of these were marked on the stone in
New Mills Yard.

The last flood he described is the
1878 one, which he covered in some
detail. His two-page account may be
considered a reliable summary because
it was written a year or two after the
event, allowing the key facts to be
assimilated, and included some considered comments made by Woodward
about the causal factors.

After a prolonged wet period, the
river level had risen to a critical level and
had taken the city by surprise on the
afternoon of Saturday 16 November.
Flooding initially affected the Heigham

Figure 24 Portrait photograph of Sir Harry Bullard,
taken about 15 years after the 1878 flood

Street area, then Westwick Street and Oak Street, where there were many occupied yards
close to the river. Before nightfall, between 3,000 and 6,000 houses in these lower-lying
areas were said to have been under several feet of water. Flooding was also reported in
parts of Colegate and Magdalen Street, caused by water 'rising from sewers'.

The key person in the quickly arranged relief operation was the Mayor, Harry Bullard
(Figure 24). He had been in post only a matter of weeks, and his brewery at Coslany
Street (founded by his father in 1837) had itself been badly hit by the flood (Figure 25).[1]

---

1   The *Norfolk Chronicle and Norwich Gazette* reported (23 November) that Messrs Bullards'
    Brewery was inundated to a great extent. The flooring of the store-room was forced up by the
    current, and thousands of casks – which were plugged on the first appearance of danger – were
    afloat, forming for time at any rate a seat of refuge for a great number of 'washed out' rats.

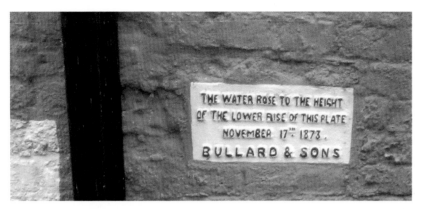

Figure 25 A stone in the river wall at the former Bullard's Brewery site near St Miles Bridge. The sign has been repainted and the original '1878' has mistakenly been changed to '1873'.

The *Eastern Daily Press* of Tuesday 19 November reported:

RAISING A RELIEF FUND – MEETING OF THE CITIZENS

The call made by the Mayor upon the citizens to attend a meeting on Monday at noon at the Guildhall, for the purpose of taking steps to relieve the sufferers, was responded to in a manner as unexampled as the need for aid was unprecedented. But the object of the meeting was for action not talk, so that the proceedings were short. The Mayor presided …

The relief fund was quickly inaugurated, and it rapidly received contributions which were all carefully recorded, amounting to over £2,000 in the first day. A network of public shelters was swiftly organised under the direction of Harry Bullard, who subsequently received fulsome praise from all sides. As a result of these and his later actions he became a city hero, going on to become elected MP and receiving a knighthood in 1887. He died in 1903.

The newspapers in those days printed few if any photographs (those that did appear were usually to record notable events such as society weddings), but that is not to say that photographs of the 1878 flood were not taken. They have turned up in other places. Most depict flooded residential streets (such as that shown in Figure 23), but one is a striking panoramic view over the roof of Colman's mustard mill, showing a wide lake stretching between King Street and Thorpe, covering what is now the Riverside area and extending downstream beyond the railway swing-bridge at Trowse (Figure 26).

The flood crept up on the city as the result of an accumulation of two weeks of rain. Woodward notes that it had followed a long period of very wet weather, with 6 inches of precipitation recorded in the city for the first 16 days of November 1878, including a heavy fall of snow on 12 November which rapidly thawed. This was coupled with an unusually high tide at Great Yarmouth on 16 November which is said to have prevented outflow of the accumulated waters.

According to the City Engineer, Mr Marshall, 'The New Mills dam was the main

Figure 26 Elevated view, probably from a chimney over Carrow Works, showing flooding in 1878. Carrow Road bridge over the railway is visible in the distance at the left edge and the railway swing bridge over the Wensum towards the right.

cause of the floods', and H. B. Woodward adds that 'whatever outlets there were became choked up with drift wood, hay, broken boats, fences and other materials'. Those observations would certainly help to explain the overtopping of the banks at Heigham, but the backed-up water farther down the river valley below Norwich must also have been a significant factor for what happened elsewhere in the city, as evidenced by the photograph taken from a high point looking over the Colman's factory.

Mercifully, by Monday 18 November the floodwaters were receding, and the *Norwich Mercury* of 23 November reported:

THE LATEST ABOUT THE FLOOD – SUBSIDENCE OF THE WATER
By Wednesday morning the flooded streets on both sides of the river were comparatively dry, though here and there, in the lowest parts, the yards and places had the appearance of swamps. The drowned-out inhabitants very speedily returned to their dwellings, and hundreds were woefully distressed at the sight which met their view. … The gardens in the Heigham district are a scene of desolation – walls have fallen, outbuildings wrecked, fowls, &c., drowned; and it will be a work of time to repair damages.

The *Norwich Argus* of 23 November stated

Mr Harry Bullard was exactly the person to deal with the crisis, and he dealt with it in a proper and liberal spirit. There was no fuming about over trivialities – he knew where to lay his hand on the wagons to get the people away from their houses; he knew where boats were to be had to get up the various riverside yards; he knew every baker in Norwich would work for him, Sunday though it was, when requested, to meet such a calamity; that grocers and drapers would furnish supplies under the circumstances; and he went to work and issued orders like one who was sure to be obeyed. Well has the Mayor inaugurated his year of office. He was admirably seconded by the Sheriff [Donald Steward Esq.], and Norwich ought to congratulate itself that, since such a misfortune was to fall upon it, a brace of brewers were Mayor and Sheriff who were so fully able to meet an emergency the horrors of which we pray may never be again experienced by our fellow-citizens.

Figure 27 Contemporary postcard view of Thorpe Station

5 Norwich in 1912

An Edwardian context

Anyone with vivid childhood memories of the 1878 flood would have reached the age of 40 or so by the time the repeat disaster visited Norwich and the surrounding area. And there must have been older people living within the affected area who, after a third of a century, could only sigh and say 'Here we go again…'.

One thing that had been remarked upon by the local newspapers in 1878 was the degree to which political differences had been temporarily set aside to deal with the crisis, such as at the launch of the relief fund.[1]

After that event there was a swift return to the rumbustiousness of local politics. The years that followed were marked by an ever-growing influence of the labour movement, and it was in 1906 that radical Norwich elected its first Labour MP.

The women's suffrage movement was also well underway. While the Edwardian period

---

1   From the *Norwich Argus*, Saturday 23 November 1878: 'It was a sight worth seeing in that old Council Chamber – the scene of so many conflicts – Tory and Whig, blatant Radical and brass-lunged Republican, jostling each other, not in anger, but in good humour, each eager to put down his name, or have it put down by the Mayor, for a sum of money named by himself for the relief of poor citizens…'

in the first decade of the twentieth century is often portrayed in retrospect as a time of complacent prosperity (albeit as the sun was setting on the British Empire), in Norwich it would have been difficult to ignore the changes that were afoot.

At a national level, the aristocracy had remained in control through the dominance of the Conservatives (Unionists) and the Liberal Party, supported not only by the landed gentry and church but by many of the better-educated working class. However, public activism was putting the ruling parties under strong pressure to reform their policies. In the 1906 General Election the Tories lost to the Liberal Party, who went on to make some significant welfare reforms before eventually becoming eclipsed by the Labour Party, which had already gained an early foothold in the city.

Since the city had got its first public sewerage system and water supply during the nineteenth century there had been moves towards progressive improvement in public health. The broadening of Norwich's manufacturing base, expansion of the suburbs and construction of the electric tram system (1899) meant a growing population could be supported, albeit with remaining areas of very poor housing, including numerous cramped residential yards in the city centre. A sign of the relative prosperity at this time was the unveiling of elaborate memorials, such as that to the fallen in the Boer War at Market Avenue erected in 1904 (Figure 28), and the statue of Sir Thomas Browne on Hay Hill of 1905 (Figure 29).

During this period there was also a naval arms race going on with Germany, and in retrospect this raising of the stakes was one of the factors that led to the First World War. While people were generally conscious of the nation's military strength, the feeling

Figure 28 Unveiling of the Boer War memorial in 1904

Figure 29 Unveiling the statue of Sir Thomas Browne in 1905, viewed through tram wires

it induced was chiefly one of security: the risk of real conflict was not widely recognised in 1912. There was a strong army presence in the city (with two large barracks in the Mousehold area), but virtually no Norwich person would have been expecting an all-consuming and prolonged war to break out within two years.

A newspaper sample

A leaf through the Norwich and Norfolk newspapers for the earlier part of 1912 offers an illuminating if random impression of what life was like, and of the local and national issues that were occupying readers at that time.

January 1912 began with a report in the *Norwich Mercury* of rumours of a military mobilisation at Aldershot. Other stories include a large cliff fall at Dover after abnormal rainfall in the previous two or three months, a knighthood for Ditchingham-based writer Rider Haggard in the New Year Honours, and news that the resident lions were to be removed from Colney Park. Later in the month we read of one of the Royal Navy's new Dreadnought battleships having been involved in a collision. The Midland & Great Northern railway company announced a fare increase. An advertisement in the newspaper offered 'Cheque books for women' available from Farrow's Bank in the Market Place, and there were numerous other adverts for pills, foods and special syrups to aid all kinds of ailment. Towards the end of the month the suffragettes were in Norwich, but plans for an appearance by Emmeline Pankhurst had to be revised after she was delayed on a boat from the USA: instead there was an address by her daughter Miss Christabel Pankhurst, who duly proclaimed 'violence was justified' and denounced the government. There was also a local meeting on Home Rule for Ireland.

Figure 30 Postcard of RMS *Ascania*, which took Norwich emigrants (among others) to Canada

In early February 1912 the *Mercury* included reports of severe frost and dense fog. A photograph was published showing a game of hockey being played on ice. An Austro-Hungarian steamer ran aground in fog on Happisburgh Sands, and a submarine did the same at Southampton. The abdication of the emperor of China was reported, as was news of a skeleton found at Ipswich which represented the earliest human remains discovered in Britain. Telegraph Lane in Thorpe was under reconstruction. Later in the month we read about Norwich emigrants leaving Thorpe Station for Southampton, where they would be catching the liner *Ascania* (Figure 30) and sailing to a new life in Ontario: the newspaper also contained a repeat advertisement seeking more people who wished to go to work there. There was the latest in a regular series of reports giving health statistics for the city, and pianos were available at 8/6 per month.

In March came the news that a million miners had gone out on strike, and there were fears being expressed about a rail strike. On top of that there were outbreaks of suffragette activism involving damage to property. Another batch of local emigrants was reported to have left, and an alleged spy of unknown nationality was caught in the Isle of Wight. Churchwardens at Great Witchingham were in trouble with the ecclesiastical authorities after it was found church pews had been sold to a pig farmer for use as sties. Pianos were now being advertised at 2/6 per week.

April was the time for the Spring Horse and Stallion Sale at the Agricultural Hall, alongside the regular cattle markets. Further news had come through of Captain Scott at the South Pole. Then on 13 April the 16th Lancers were reported to have had to make a sudden departure from their cavalry parade because they were needed to control riots at northern collieries. On 17 April came the dramatic news of the sinking of the *Titanic* on her maiden voyage.

In May there was a Philharmonic Concert at St Andrew's Hall featuring the famous cellist Sir Pablo Casals. There was a report on a public demonstration of cooking using electricity, and an article entitled 'How thin people may put on flesh'. Sadly there were quite frequent stories of local suicides and occasional murders. The naval arms race is hinted at in a proud report that Britain now had over 100 torpedo boat destroyers in the North Sea. Industrial unrest continued with the Transport Workers' strike. The City Council announced the intended laying out of St Gregory's Churchyard, and the death occurred of the former Liberal MP Sir George White. The Anglo-Netherlands Sugar Corporation was founded. The *Titanic* enquiry got underway.

June 1912 brought the death and funeral of the popular Norwich cleric Bishop Sheepshanks. There are several accounts of 'unfortunate accidents' on the roads, such as when a woman was knocked down and killed by a motor tri-car on the corner of Chapelfield East. There was another incident elsewhere involving runaway horses. There is an account of a flogging at Norwich Prison, and news of a new motor fire engine and steam float for the city.[2] It was Pageant Week, with a production by director Nugent Monk. A fishing trawler was moored in the city for the training of Norwich lads.[3]

In July an editorial stated that 'National defence continues to engage public attention', while disquiet was expressed at the local drilling of Territorial soldiers on Sundays. The success of the City's electricity undertaking was proclaimed, and it was announced the City Council was to be provided with additional

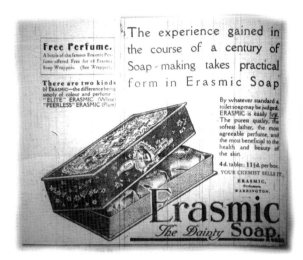

Figure 31 Advertisement in the *Norwich Mercury*, July 1912

office accommodation. There would be a new Fish Market, a new City School and a Technical Institute. Cantley Sugar Factory was by now under construction. Some local horses in a field were killed by a bolt of lightning. Large advertisements encouraged readers to buy Erasmic – the dainty soap (Figure 31).

During August 1912 the *Mercury* covered various public events in Norwich, including the annual athletic meeting at the Earlham Road Ground, the National Catholic Congress which met that year in the city, and an aviation display in which Mr Hucks flew in his monoplane from Gowing's Farm in Lower Hellesdon. It was announced that major army manoeuvres were planned in East Anglia later in the year, including the introduction of a military airship. The weather moved into focus when an editorial article referred to the lack of sun and the prolonged period of cold and wet compared with the abnormal heat of the previous year's summer. There was a report on 'sweltering heat' in parts of Russia.

Then on 28 August we read the first report of a torrential deluge ...

---

2   The hose spouts on certain bridges (see photos of St Miles Bridge and St George's Bridge in Appendix 1) were added at this time to allow the steam float to take on water.
3   This was the start of Norwich Sea Cadets: the group finally moved from the river in 2018.

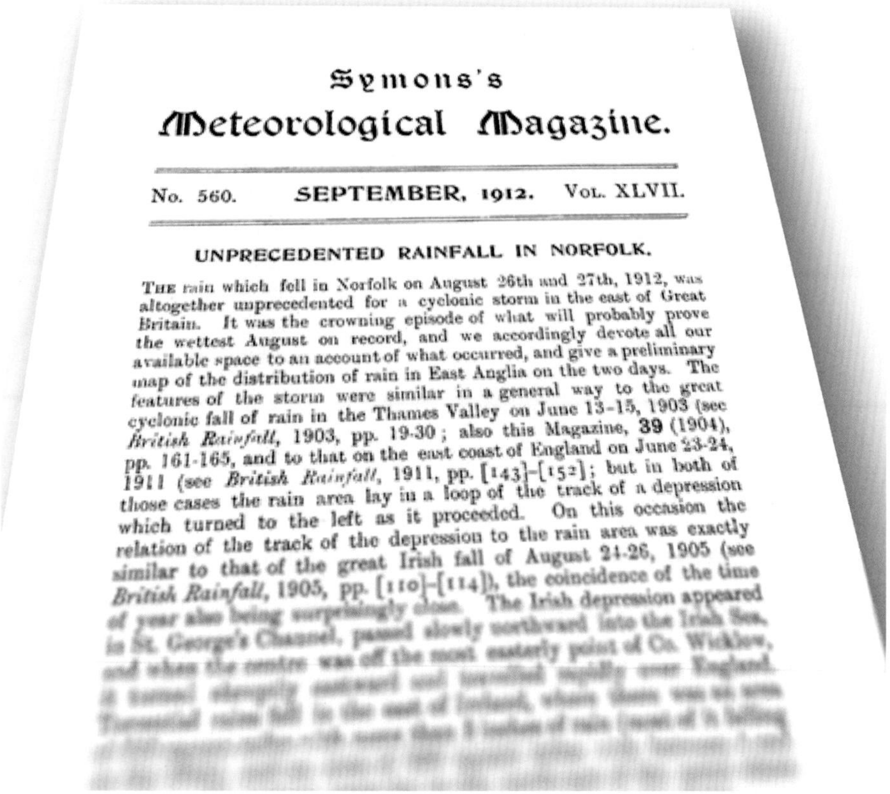

Symons's

Meteorological Magazine.

No. 560.   SEPTEMBER, 1912.   Vol. XLVII.

UNPRECEDENTED RAINFALL IN NORFOLK.

THE rain which fell in Norfolk on August 26th and 27th, 1912, was altogether unprecedented for a cyclonic storm in the east of Great Britain. It was the crowning episode of what will probably prove the wettest August on record, and we accordingly devote all our available space to an account of what occurred, and give a preliminary map of the distribution of rain in East Anglia on the two days. The features of the storm were similar in a general way to the great cyclonic fall of rain in the Thames Valley on June 13-15, 1903 (see *British Rainfall*, 1903, pp. 19-30; also this Magazine, **39** (1904), pp. 161-165, and to that on the east coast of England on June 23-24, 1911 (see *British Rainfall*, 1911, pp. [143]-[152]; but in both of those cases the rain area lay in a loop of the track of a depression which turned to the left as it proceeded. On this occasion the relation of the track of the depression to the rain area was exactly similar to that of the great Irish fall of August 24-26, 1905 (see *British Rainfall*, 1905, pp. [110]-[114]), the coincidence of the time of year also being surprisingly close. The Irish depression appeared in St. George's Channel, passed slowly northward into the Irish Sea, and when the centre was off the most easterly point of Co. Wicklow, it turned sharply eastward and travelled rapidly over England. Torrential rains fell in the east of Ireland, where there was an area of high ground rather more than 3 inches of rain (most of it falling

Figure 32 Early report of the weather event in *Symons's Meteorological Magazine*, September 1912

Figure 33 Postcard view towards the Lower Close as
reproduced in *Fisher's Almanac*

6 A storm breaks

Here is the weather forecast ...

If in 1912 there had been available the detailed day-to-day weather forecasts we are accustomed to today, it would be interesting to see what might have been said on the evening of 25 August, perhaps to warn the people of Norwich and Norfolk of what was about to happen. There is in fact no record of any forewarning of what turned out to be a remarkable 24-hour weather event beginning on the morning of Monday 26 August, albeit one that had followed on from an extended period that had already been remarked on at the time as an unusually cold and wet summer.

We do however have a commendably detailed retrospective meteorological account of what occurred in the eastern counties on that and the following day, as well as comprehensive national climatic data to provide a context for this more local phenomenon. This is thanks to the high standard of routine data collection at the time, especially in regard to rainfall, and to the labour-intensive administrative efforts of the British Rainfall Organization.

... in retrospect

Not only did an initial technical report of the storm appear swiftly in print in September 1912[1] (Figure 33), but a more detailed paper based on a full statistical reappraisal of data was produced within three months of the event. It contained an hour-by-hour analysis of the rainfall as accurately recorded by volunteers[2] at 262 measuring stations spread across East Anglia, covering a rectangular area measuring 191 km by 146 km (113 by 86 miles) – containing about 21,240 sq km (8,200 sq miles) of land. This paper of January 1913, authored by H. R. Mill, was prepared with precision and rigour, and he had access to enough data to have the luxury of rejecting certain of the raw meteorological readings that could not be verified against adjacent results.[3]

The main rainfall data conventionally consisted of accurate 24-hour readings routinely taken each day at 9 am, but in this case many correspondents had taken extra readings at other times of day because of the fear that their rain gauges would overflow. As it happened, the main rainfall event was largely confined to one calendar day, Monday 26 August, but split between what would normally be two measurements – rainfall that fell before 9 am (officially counted as 25 August) and that falling later in the day (collected on 27 August and ascribed to 26 August).

In meteorological jargon, what happened was a widespread extremely heavy cyclonic rainfall event. Reported observations showed that the onset of the rain occurred progressively later the further north-westwards you were, such that it began at 1 am in the Ipswich area, at around 4 am in Norwich, and at 6 am in the area of the Wash (the onset crossed the county at about 33 kph, or 20 mph). The duration of the rainfall was around 24 hours over a large area of Norfolk, and it was accompanied by very strong wind. For some of this period the intensity of rainfall was between 25 and 50mm (1 to 2 inches) each hour. This is considerable, but somewhat below what can be experienced for short periods during severe thunderstorms.

The telling plot is that showing the total rainfall amount during the whole 24-hour event (Figure 34). It is evident that by the early hours of Tuesday 27 August, much of the eastern half of Norfolk had received more than 100 mm (4 in) of rain, over a 'splash' extending 95 km from Wells in the north to Debenham in the south, and from the Watton area eastwards for at least 52 km to the North Sea coast and beyond. And the total rainfall increased towards the centre of this area, such that it exceeded 190 mm (7.5 in) over about 170 sq km (65 sq miles) centred on the very wettest spot. That was at Brundall, thankfully downstream from the city, or the scale of subsequent flood damage would surely have been even greater.

Mill's paper included a calculation of the total volume of water dropped on Norfolk during this 24-hour period (equivalent to some 685,000 million litres) of which about two-thirds would eventually have found its way into the Rivers Yare or Bure. When that total volume was compared with other events in the British rainfall record, including in the Lake District, it was found to be unprecedented.

---

1 In *Symons's Meteorological Magazine*.
2 A significant number of the correspondents seemed to be clergymen with weather stations in their rectory gardens.
3 It was published in the *Quarterly Journal of the Royal Meteorological Society*.

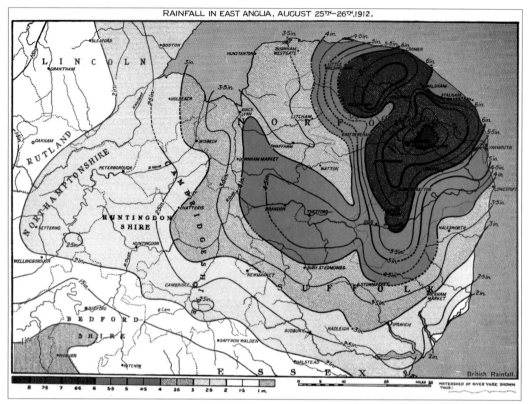

RAINFALL IN EAST ANGLIA, AUGUST 25TH–26TH,1912.

Figure 34 Accurate plot of rainfall intensity during the storm, published in *British Rainfall 1912*. There are several subtly different versions of this plot in different publications based on reworking of the same data.

It is worth noting that only 35 per cent of that water contributed to the flow down the Wensum valley that somehow had to find its way through the city of Norwich, as most of the rain fell in areas downstream from the city. That was indeed fortunate. The city's share nevertheless amounted to about 165,000 million litres, weighing some 165 million tonnes.[4] This volume can be visualised as the equivalent of about 100 full water tanker lorries for each man, woman or child living in the city at the time (Figure 35).

It is appropriate to consider how the meteorological situation differed from that which led to the earlier 'Great Flood'. In November 1878 the county had received a record 200 mm (8 in) of rainfall in one month in the form of a succession of wet days over a 10–14 day period leading to saturation of the ground, culminating in two very wet days which had caused a major flood owing to run-off into the watercourses. During August 1912, while a similar total amount of rain fell in the east part of the county to that experienced in November 1878, it all came to earth in barely 24 hours.

---

4   This figure is about 20 times the maximum daily amount of water it was estimated could be accommodated by the river channel at Fye Bridge without overflowing (some 8,200 million litres per day).

Figure 35 A representation of the volume of floodwater arriving in Norwich for each member of the population as the result of the storm

Wide-ranging implications of the weather

We have already noted that the 1912 event occurred towards the end of a month that had been characterised by exceptionally cold and dull weather. In fact in August 1912 the average temperature was more than 5°C lower than it had been in August 1911, which conversely had been the culmination of an exceptionally warm and dry summer (see Figure 36).

Some commentators (Kendon and Prior) have suggested this combination of heat and drought, followed a year later by cold and floods, was a significant factor contributing to the political and social tension that affected the United Kingdom in 1911 and 1912.

A physical explanation for the unusually cold summer of 1912 has also since been identified. It closely followed a major volcanic eruption in Alaska in June, which spread fine ash into the stratosphere for several months, partially masking out the sun for the following months, with a major effect on the weather that year.

Such a connection – from a geological event via the weather to social unrest – adds a more global dimension to the local principle that 'geology drives everything'. In this case it was the subterranean conditions in one part of the world that profoundly influenced the behaviour and feelings of people living thousands of kilometres away.

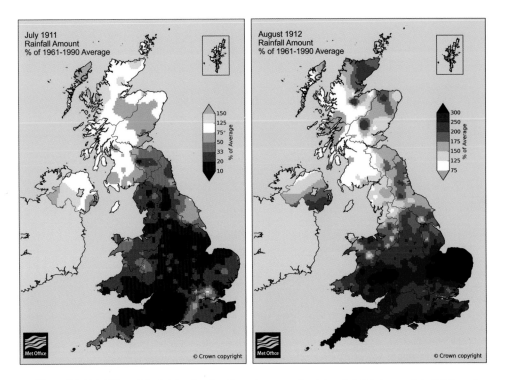

Figure 36 Met Office plot of data showing the extreme contrast in rainfall between July 1911 and August 1912

Figure 37 A family being rescued (strangely, in water that
hardly seems deep enough for a boat), while a helper glances at
the camera

Figure 38 Extract from John Crome's painting of the
River Wensum, 1814

7 Politics, posing and the public good

The social context

The flood in Norwich came at a sort of hinge point in terms of both British social attitudes and civic planning. There had been concern expressed for decades in official circles about the state of much of the city's housing stock: it was recognised that many people were living in cramped conditions with inadequate drainage provision, including (but not confined to) the many overcrowded yards between Oak Street and the river. The view from the river had for many years been of somewhat tumbledown and rustic dwellings (see Figure 38), all very picturesque, but decreasingly acceptable.

While a public water supply and sewerage system for Norwich had eventually been constructed by the 1870s, many homes had yet to be connected to it. In reality, only feeble and localised progress had been made in dealing with the housing problem, and it had perhaps tacitly been accepted by politicians for years that the poorer classes lived like that. That attitude of complacency was now changing, and the Great Flood turned out to act as something of a wake-up call.

At a larger scale, Norwich was in a process of modernisation, manifested in the Oak Street/Coslany Street area by the opening in 1882 of a new (third) railway station built on land upstream from New Mills: the site had at the time of the 1878 flood been open marshy ground crossed by drainage channels. The old timber-framed corn mill buildings

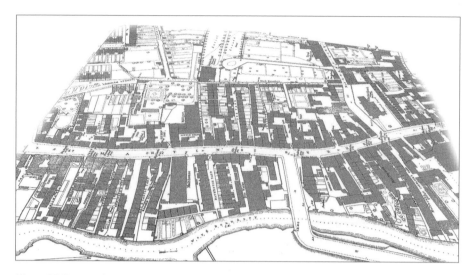

Figure 39 Perspective extract from Ordnance Survey 1:500 scale map of 1883, showing the high density of yards on the river frontage off what is now Oak Street. In this orientation we are looking eastwards down the line of what is now St Crispin's Road from near Barn Road roundabout, with north to the left.

had been dismantled from the dam in 1897 and replaced by a new brick-built pumping station. This made clever use of water power to compress air and thus move sewage from the lower parts of the city.[1]

This progress was being overseen and governed by an increasingly powerful and professional administration (which followed the introduction of the Norwich Corporation Act of 1889) which was able to consider large-scale changes to parts of the city. The council's developing plans for improvement were at this stage largely unencumbered by serious conservation concerns. There was little appreciation outside antiquarian circles (at least until the 1920s) of the value of the city's historic heritage, other than the desirability of preserving the more obvious medieval buildings. In retrospect the 1912 flood can be seen as another catalyst that led to the acceleration of the physical improvements that became manifest following the First World War.

Who suffered most?

It goes without saying that as the water levels rose rapidly and overflowed the riverbanks on the morning of Tuesday 27 August, the great majority of the homes flooded were those occupied by poorer people in the central parts of the city. Many lived in those yards near the river off Coslany Street and Oak Street (Figure 39), but also all along Heigham Street and the adjacent terraced streets, where the impact of the overspilling was propor-

---

1 The dam itself was little changed. Turbines were mounted in the former wheel races beneath the northern half of the dam, and the overflow sluices were left in place beneath the southern half. This pumping station and its machinery survive today.

Figure 40 Hand-coloured
postcard view of
Midland Street

tionately more severe than
elsewhere (for reasons
which are explained in the
next chapter).

While it was not a
dissimilar situation to that
in 1878, the floodwater had
already exceeded the 1878
level by mid-afternoon on
the Tuesday. By the time it
had at last stopped rising in
the early hours of Wednesday 28 August, there had appeared a lake approximately 700 m
wide at Heigham and nearly 400 m wide at Carrow – and this unavoidably inundated a
large number of low-lying homes. Many hundreds of houses now had deep muddy water
standing in their living rooms.

In all, approximately 15,000 people and 3,650 premises were affected, of which it was
later counted 380 were shops or pubs, 33 places of worship or schools and 57 factories.[2]
Not only did residents lose their possessions, their animals and use of their homes, many
working people must also have been unable to get to their place of work to earn any
money (Figure 40).

How the flooding was reported

We have already made reference to the widely available *Illustrated Record of the Great
Flood* which, although undated, was evidently printed only a few days after the event
and made available for sale at 3d as part of the fund-raising operation.[3] In the foreword,
the publishers freely state that the record 'has perforce had to be culled from the various
newspapers' which they said gave 'very graphic descriptions from day to day'.

It is apparent that many of the accounts of the 1912 flood published in recent years
have drawn from this source. Unsurprisingly for the time, the writing is characterised
by a certain melodramatic style. For example, it describes the 'blank despair' caused by
the 'ruthless onslaught' of the 'terrifying calamity' which was the flood, and other such
superlative descriptions invoke the extremes of human danger and heroism involved in
the 'prodigious work of rescue', such as those who 'plunged into the seething waters up
to their eyes'.

We can also be a little circumspect about the more florid statements, such as that at

---

2   These figures are from the official final report prepared in November 1913 for the City
    Council's Flood Relief Committee.
3   Similar accounts appeared in local periodicals, such as *Fisher's Almanac*, produced by George
    Fisher and sold from his tobacconist's shop on the corner of Barn Road and Westwick Street.

one time 'the cathedral was actually in danger' from the flood, and the city was 'absolutely cut off' and 'an island'. It seems less than literally true that 'many streets caved in' and that 'everywhere was the piteous wailing of children', notwithstanding the grim and distressing reality of the inundation itself, and the residue of filth that must have covered everything below the water level in the affected parts of the city.

It is interesting to look again at the newspapers of the day and see how the story broke – initially coming over as something of a catch-up exercise by reporters in comparison with those who must have experienced it first hand. In the *Eastern Evening News* of Tuesday 27 August the writer admits:

> In the absence of telegraphic and train communication, we are not in a position to state the effect of the storm on the country around Norwich, and the damage in the city has been so general that it is difficult to get details. There is scarcely a house where the water has not got in somewhere …. the streets in the low-lying parts were flooded, and the water in many cases entered gardens and houses.

In the Wednesday and later editions a fuller picture of the disaster emerges, and the reports cover in detail the City Council's actions and also the public appeal for donations, not just of money but in kind. In Thursday's *Eastern Evening News* we read in an editorial column:

> No appeal has been made to the citizens of Norwich within this generation that calls for a more generous and prompt response than that which we issue this morning from the acting Lord Mayor and the committee appointed yesterday. The need is a need which transcends imagination, both in its urgency and its imagination; and the response to the appeal should come in a flood, deep and wide but happily beneficent.

As a rule, the newspapers of the day still printed few action photographs, presumably

Figure 41 Milk delivery to Dial House, Heigham Street, with the modern view for comparison taken 106 years later to the day

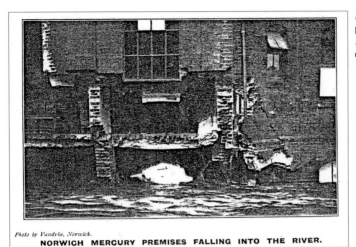

Photo by *Vandyke, Norwich.*
NORWICH MERCURY PREMISES FALLING INTO THE RIVER.

Figure 42 Published photograph of the *Norwich Mercury*'s damaged print works

because of the slowness of processing coupled with the longstanding reliance on words to convey the story. However the *Eastern Evening News* did publish a selection of views of the floods from 28 August onwards. These featured certain streets and damaged bridges, and some more generic (and on the face of it reassuring) pictures of tradesmen making deliveries (Figure 41) and of rescued families. Hopefully it was not simply commercial rivalry on the part of the *Evening News* that made it print two different close-up views of the damaged *Norwich Mercury* works at St George's within the first week (Figure 42). The *Mercury* itself did appear, but included an apology about the adverse effects on production (Figure 43).

The *Illustrated Record of the Great Flood* includes photographs credited to Messrs

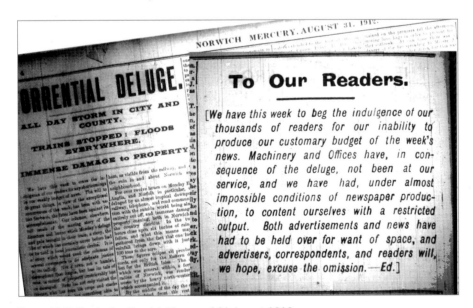

Figure 43 Notice in the *Norwich Mercury* of 31 August 1912

Figure 44 Postcard with what appears to be a carefully posed picture of a food delivery in Lothian Street

Vandyke and Swain, and comments that some were taken 'under very difficult circumstances, and from positions in which the operator was in no small danger and discomfort'. Those are only a selection of the large number of contemporary photographs of the 1912 flood that can be found in collections today, many of them published originally as postcards, and these are a useful resource.

It should not however be assumed all photographs stand as an impartial record: there have been suggestions that one or two purporting to show rescues in progress may have been specially staged for the cameraman.[4] Certainly some of the pictures include people of status who are posing for the camera, such as shop proprietors in Magdalen Street, or a civic worthy delivering a food parcel in Lothian Street (Figure 44).

Civic organisation

Reading the detailed accounts in internal City Council documents of the time, we cannot help but be impressed by the administrative urgency and level of organisation with which the crisis was dealt. This time round it was more a question of an organisational machine swinging into action than one person calling all the orders, as had Harry Bullard in 1878. The Lord Mayor (Henry Copeman) happened to be away abroad during late August 1912,[5] so it was left to a deputy councillor (George Chamberlin) and the Town Clerk

---

4   There is a picture showing Constable Albert Farrow overseeing the rescue by ladder of a trapped family in what appears to be ankle-deep water (see Figure 37). That this photo was staged was suggested by Maurice Morson in his book *A Force Remembered*.

(Arnold Miller) to convene an emergency committee, which first met formally on the Wednesday morning.

The potential danger of the rising river had been recognised early on Monday 26 August during the storm, when all the sluices at the New Mills dam were manually opened in an attempt to maximise the amount of water that could pass though – and not least to try to reduce the dangerous sideways pressure on the structure.[6] For the next 48 hours, strenuous efforts were made to keep the same sluices free from obstruction by floating debris, which included large bundles of hay, long deals of wood (from nearby timber yards) and the remains of more than 15 boats. The importance of preventing blockage of the weir was probably a lesson learned from the experience of the 1878 flood.

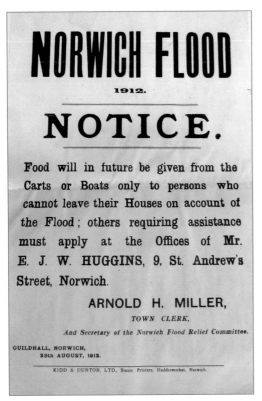

NORWICH FLOOD

1912.

NOTICE.

Food will in future be given from the Carts or Boats only to persons who cannot leave their Houses on account of the Flood ; others requiring assistance must apply at the Offices of Mr. E. J. W. HUGGINS, 9, St. Andrew's Street, Norwich.

ARNOLD H. MILLER,

TOWN CLERK,

And Secretary of the Norwich Flood Relief Committee.

GUILDHALL, NORWICH,
29th AUGUST, 1912.

KIDD & DUNTON, LTD., Steam Printers, Maddermarket, Norwich.

Figure 45 Early poster issued on 29 August 1912

During Tuesday 27 August, even before the emergency committee had met, there was frenetic but ordered activity, making detailed arrangements and issuing instructions. The active players were not only City Council employees, but also the police, fire brigade (then part of the police force), a squadron of soldiers sent down from Britannia Barracks and many civilian volunteers.[7]

The action was focused initially on the necessary rescuing of people from their homes in the lower-lying areas and setting up a series of shelters, mainly in schools, for the roughly 7,000 people who were flooded out. The next job was ensuring family members were accounted for and that there was provision for food and blankets, both for people in shelters and those who were remaining in their homes. All of them were also provided with candles and matches.

---

5 The deputy Lord Mayor too was absent initially.

6 By the time the water had overflowed New Mills the next day, the bridges at Lakenham and Trowse had already been washed away, and there must have been grave concern about the stability of the New Mills dam.

7 In a scrapbook collected by the Town Clerk (now in Norfolk Record Office) we have a type-written account submitted by the City Engineer dated 5 September 1912 detailing all the actions and movements of members of his department. The only rescuer to have lost his life was not a public employee, but a 46-year-old local fish porter, George Brodie.

Figure 46 Wooden paving blocks being collected from Duke Street north of the bridge

It was realised from midday on Monday that the flood crisis was reaching an unprecedented level. The water continued to rise incessantly for 42 hours, exceeding the 1878 mark during the afternoon, creeping up further throughout Tuesday 27 and finally peaking at around 3 am in the early hours of Wednesday 28 August. Well before then there were families finding themselves trapped on the upper floors of flooded homes, some needing rescue. This was achieved throughout Tuesday and overnight using a combination of wheeled transport (horse-drawn carts) and commandeered rowing boats (see the poster in Figure 45). The former faced the problem of moving through deep water on surfaces that could not be seen, and the latter were at times in danger of being carried away by swirling currents, or being pierced by railings or other sharp submerged hazards that were invisible in the dark.

Meanwhile, the public services relied upon by the city as a whole were in jeopardy. Pumping of water from the river to supply the waterworks was stopped for 36 hours from around 6 pm on Tuesday 27, and the Mousehold and Lakenham reservoirs became quickly exhausted after panic drawing-off of water by the understandably concerned public. Drinking water had by this time turned brown, largely because of peat. Flooding of the electricity works located next to the river at Duke Street was inevitable. It was delayed for a time by vigorous pumping, until the evening when the battle was lost, and electric lighting in the city failed at 8.45 pm. Somehow, the public piped gas supply was maintained throughout.[8]

8 The electricity supply was restored at 6 am on Thursday morning while the dynamos at Duke

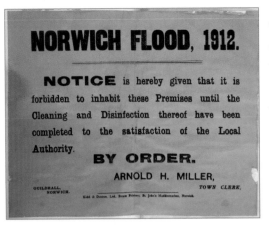

NORWICH FLOOD, 1912.

NOTICE is hereby given that it is forbidden to inhabit these Premises until the Cleaning and Disinfection thereof have been completed to the satisfaction of the Local Authority.

BY ORDER.

ARNOLD H. MILLER,

GUILDHALL,
NORWICH.   *TOWN CLERK.*

Kidd & Denton, Ltd., Steam Printers, St. John's Maddermarket, Norwich.

Figure 47 A poster issued as the flood was abating

Transport connections to the city by rail and across it by tram were of course seriously disrupted, and many roads within the flooded area became impassable for wheeled and foot traffic, because of standing water, damage to manholes and culverts, or because wood block paving had floated out of position (Figure 46).

By Thursday 29 August arrangements had been made to meet the immediate practical needs of all the flood victims, and it was decreed that all affected homes would be inspected by the sanitary department (Figure 47). The following day it was announced that food would be given to all residents in the flooded area on application at St Andrew's Hall from 12 noon, using a system of clipped tickets. That evening a register of losses was started (to be compiled district by district), and the following day the decision was made to make bread handouts available up to at least 5 September, and also to supply brushes, soap and flannel to all affected households to assist in clean-up operations (Figure 48).

By the end of Saturday 31 August much of the pumping-out had at last been done. By that stage the City Engineer had issued about 50 dangerous building notices.

In the following days the shelters were progressively able to be closed as the number of refugees reduced and people were able to return home. Nevertheless, there were still 1,400 refugees (mainly children) being looked after on 11 September, 16 days after the flood.

To OWNERS AND OCCUPIERS
of

FLOODED HOUSES.

Instructions as to Purifying Houses.

Damp paper to be stripped off. Filth to be removed above and below floors. Dirty and damaged plaster to be removed.

An excellent method of hastening the drying of boarded floors in houses affected by the flood is to remove some of the floor boards at intervals, and leave the openings so made exposed to the air. A brick below the floor level should be removed, which will provide for a free circulation of air. Doors and windows should be kept wide open.

H. COOPER PATTIN,
Medical Officer of Health.

Guildhall, Norwich,
September, 1912.

Gibbs & Waller, Ltd., Lithographers, Printers, and Bookbinders, Colgate Street, Norwich.

Street were still under water, thanks to a temporary cable laid to connect the works there to the private generation facility at Caley's factory at Chapelfield.

Figure 48 Practical advice from the Medical Officer

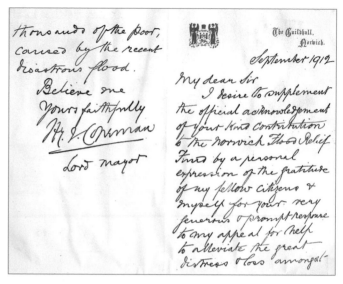

Figure 49
Handwritten letter
of thanks to a donor
from the Lord Mayor

Appeals to the public

Apart from the necessary urgent organisation of the rescue effort and emergency accommodation, an important task of the Flood Relief Committee was to coordinate a relief fund, and subsequently to decide how the collected money was spent. On Saturday 31 August the Lord Mayor was authorised to write to the newspapers declaring the Norwich Flood Relief Fund open. Generous early sums were donated by the King and local notables, and after this was publicised the money duly started to pour in from other sources (Figure 49). All sums received were carefully recorded.

Two days later, in the light of the picture that had by that time emerged about extensive damage elsewhere in Norfolk, the emergency committee had to make the awkward decision that the fund would only be used for the city and not the county. To ensure the relief effort could push on without waiting on the committee's formal authorisation of each item of expenditure, it was also necessary to arrange a loan from Barclays Bank, which was done on 3 September. By the following day, the committee was told all affected premises had been visited to assess claims for damages. By this stage half of the shelters were able to be discontinued, and by 9 September all but two were closed down.

The final report of the Flood Relief Committee more than a year later[9] recorded the total subscribed to the flood fund as just under £25,500, of which £13,000 was awarded as compensation for 'household, trade and allotment losses', with a total of 211 applications dealt with for serious damage to houses, out of the 3,650 affected. It is evident from the town clerk's scrapbook that a significant number of claims on the relief fund were rejected.

In the end it was necessary for the City Council to buy up 13 wholly uninhabitable properties. This was a prelude to the purchase of a number of other riverside properties during the next decade, as part of the Council's determined effort to get to grips with the risk of future flooding.

---

9   Dated 11 November 1913.

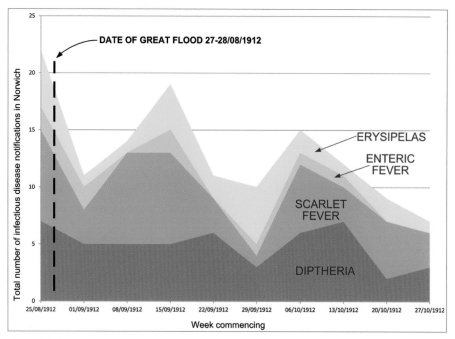

Figure 50 Plot showing the total occurrence of infectious disease in the city, split between the four infections noted, for the weeks following the flood

Public health

Over the whole period of the flooding and beyond, the Medical Officer of Health had maintained accurate records of the number of cases of infectious diseases, notably diphtheria, scarlet fever, enteric fever and erysipelas. It was remarkable that there was no sign of any significant increase in cases (see Figure 50) during the period. The death rate for the same period each year for the city fluctuated around the average of 10 persons per 1,000 population, with absolutely no discernible influence of the flood event. In a paper published in the journal *Public Health*[10] the officer stated, 'When it is remembered that the flooded area includes within its boundaries much of the worst property and of our poorest folk, the figures representative of the incidence of disease among at least 12,500 people cannot be deemed other than as satisfactory.'

Following the formation of the special committee to act on future flood prevention and housing, a final report on the 1912 flood was completed, dated 11 November 1913, and signed off by the Chairman, Henry J. Copeman (Figure 51). Without any hint of

Figure 51 Henry J. Copeman, Lord Mayor of Norwich 1911–12

10 Dated March 1913.

irony or insensitivity, the final sentence in the report stated that 'to some extent therefore the flood has had the effect of improving the conditions in the poorest parts of the city'.

Figure 52 Aftermath of the flood at a house in King Street

Figure 53 City Station during the flood. The southward view from near the end of the platform, with water flowing from left to right.

8 Understanding how it happened

How the water came and went

In this chapter I focus less on the human impacts of the Great Flood and more on the physical distribution and depth of the floodwater. We will be seeking to understand exactly how the water accumulated then subsequently drained away during that fateful week, and how this exceptional happening related to the way the dynamic river behaves during more normal times.

Such an approach is not a mere academic exercise: this understanding is the key to being able to design measures to stop it happening again. That was the task given to the City Engineer by the Flood Relief and Housing Committee, which was formed in October 1912 and continued to do its work in the years following the First World War.

We have looked at the exceptional meteorological background, but what exactly was the effect of adding all that water to the river system in 24 hours?

Looking at the flood levels

Water will always find its own level, but flooding occurs when it does so in an uncontrolled way within the dynamic drainage system.

Figure 54 A typical flood plate, on the
downstream side of St Miles Bridge

The water levels during the 1912 flood were far from being the same throughout the whole city. As this was a fluvial rather than tidal flood (the water descending from higher ground into Norwich, rather than rising from the sea), it might reasonably be expected that the absolute level of the standing or flowing water was higher on the upstream side of the city than further downstream. The question is, by how much?

If we can establish the absolute floodwater levels at various points across the city in 1912 we will have a powerful means of plotting and understanding the extent of the flooding, not just on a plan (viewed from above) but in the third dimension (viewed from the side). It is the floodwater elevation, which we will express in metres AOD, that is the parameter that matters most in determining whether a particular home or street is at risk.

Thankfully the meticulous work in the City Engineer's Department of the time has left us accurate records that allow us to plot and compare relative levels of floodwater in different parts of the city. Most visibly, there is the physical legacy of a collection of identical lozenge-shaped flood marker plates to be found to this day attached to river walls and bridge abutments through the city and slightly beyond.

It might be supposed that a few of these plates were lost over the years as the result of replacement of bridges and related bank reconstruction (such as when the replacement Duke Street Bridge was built in 1972),[1] but 12 remain to my knowledge — besides the multiple flood record plate at new Mills Yard described in Chapter 2. They are all from the same double-trapezium shaped casting (Figure 54) and are all illustrated in Appendix 1.[2]

There is at the time of writing still something of a mystery about how these most useful markers came to be put up and under whose authority, as no supporting documentation specifically referring to the plates has yet turned up during my searches through City Council records held at the Norfolk Record Office. Given the prominence of most of them on public assets, it seems most likely they were placed by the City Engineer, but it is less certain exactly when – whether soon after the flood before any temporary water marks were lost, or perhaps much later when certain river works were in progress. At least some of the plates (such as that at Fye Bridge) must have been fixed or refixed in the 1930s after construction of the sections of river wall to which they are now attached, which raises the question as to how the level to fix them was determined.[3]

---

1 George Plunkett's photographs of the original bridge from the 1930s, however, show no signs of flood plates on the abutments.
2 There are further examples on the River Yare (in areas not included in this study) such as at Cringleford Bridge and Keswick Mill.
3 During the research for this project I saw two drawings by the City Engineer's Department dated 1920, showing proposed bridge reconstructions (see drawing in Appendix 5). They recorded the 1912 flood levels at each bridge (including Duke Street and Whitefriars bridges

The publicly provided flood level markers are supplemented by three further plates, presumably of private origin, that are mounted on affected buildings more distant from the river. These permanent markers are of value because they are in useful non-riverside locations upstream, centrally and downstream in relation to the city centre, filling in gaps between other accurate flood plates. The first is a brass plate inside St Barnabas Church on Russell Street,[4] the second is a stone set in the external wall of a building at no. 20 Colegate, and the third is a stone marker in the Laurence Scott factory in Hardy Road. It was originally on an external wall but is now in a corridor following the addition of a factory extension (see Appendix 1). There may be others waiting to be found.

A major contribution by the City Engineer is a report produced in 1919 for the Flood Prevention and Housing Committee, outlining his scheme for river widening. This contained a detailed engineering analysis of water volumes, river dimensions and most importantly flood levels for the city and further downstream,[5] both for the situation in 1912 and for a hypothetical repeat event after implementation of his proposals for reducing the risk. This report was subsequently updated by his successor (with costed proposals) when presented to the General Purposes Committee in 1929.

A further source of information is the records kept at Norwich Waterworks, where the level of the river at the position of the water intakes opposite Sweetbriar Marshes was monitored. The specific relative levels noted during the 1912 flood were mentioned in the Public Health paper referred to at the end of Chapter 7.

Last but not least, the existence of a considerable number of contemporary photographs of the 1912 flood offers us a further means of obtaining flood level data from other locations, albeit in an indirect and less precise ways: by closely inspecting the images in conjunction with historic Ordnance Survey maps. The box below and overleaf outlines the method. Some of these photographs are also sufficiently clear for us to observe the direction in which water was flowing (see Figure 53).

Obtaining flood level data from photographs

- The first stage is accurately to identify the particular photograph viewpoint, then to look at the contemporary OS map for that location (initially the 25 inch edition of 1907) to obtain recorded level data, usually from spot levels in roads or from bench marks on buildings.
- Visual assessment of the water depth (or its position on walls, posts or fences) in relation to these spot levels often enables the water level (in feet AOD) to be estimated to within about 6 in or 150 mm (see example in Figure 55). Photographs offering insufficient

---

where there are no plates now), so we now know that the flood levels must have been carefully recorded. When those values are converted to modern levels, they closely match the flood plate levels recently measured (see the list in Appendix 2).

4 This church had only been built six years before the flood arrived.
5 Norwich City Council's responsibility over the river extends as far as Hardley Cross near Loddon.

visible data, or where the highest water level cannot sufficiently reliably be inferred, were discarded for the purposes of this analysis.

- The next stage is to make an adjustment for the pre-1920s OD levels used on older editions of the Ordnance Survey. This is best done by applying a conversion factor based on a comparison of the recorded values for nearby bench marks where these are shown on both older and more recent editions of the map. (In Norwich city centre this usually results in subtraction of about 1.3 ft from the original level.)
- Finally, all results have then to be converted to modern metric units.

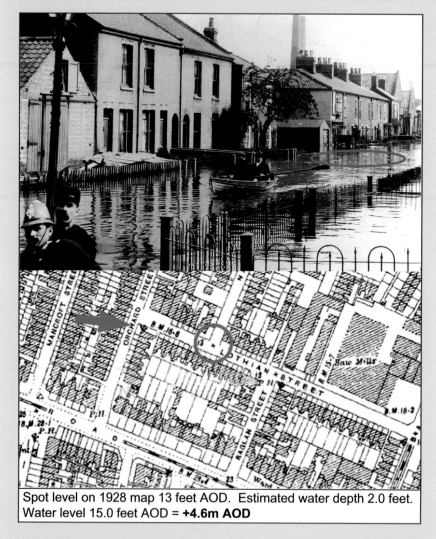

Spot level on 1928 map 13 feet AOD. Estimated water depth 2.0 feet. Water level 15.0 feet AOD = **+4.6m AOD**

Figure 55 Example of estimating the flood level from a photograph (of Lothian Street)

A sound analysis

In spite of the apparent vastness of the event, it can in principle be represented by a simple model which allows a calculation to be made of the volumes of water involved.

At any point, the depth of water (and its local impact) will be the balance between what is flowing in from 'upstream' and what is flowing out. Encouraging the water to 'get away' may reduce local flooding but will inevitably increase the inflow further downstream, potentially increasing flooding there. It was recognised at the time that Norwich's problem needed to be looked at on a citywide basis. The areas worst affected by flooding were simply those where there was the greatest bottleneck in the drainage system.

The City Engineer's calculation of the volume of water falling into the catchment area upstream of the city during a 12-hour period at the height of the storm was 17,000 million gallons (77,500 million litres), which can be compared with the maximum discharge of the river of 900 million gallons (just over 4,000 million litres) during the same period, measured at Foundry Bridge during the flood (this is taken as the absolute capacity of the river).[6]

Figure 56 Nineteenth-century photo of Anderson's Meadow as a flood plain before it was filled and raised. The view is towards Drayton Road and Stone Road.

---

6   It was also calculated that the short section of the Wensum valley from Hellesdon Bridge to New Mills alone accumulated 600 million gallons during that 12-hour period, which would have used up two-thirds of the discharge capacity of the river through the city had not that section of the river been able to act as a flood reservoir. It was pointed out that 'any improvement in the river channel above the city boundary, to enable flood waters to pass more quickly, would therefore increase flooding below.'

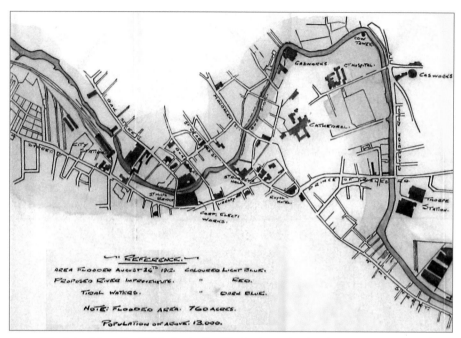

Figure 57 Extract from the 1920 plan by the City Engineer showing the extent of the 1912 flood in light blue (the full plan is reproduced in Appendix 5)

What this means is that only about one-nineteenth of the rainwater that fell during the storm ran off straight away into the river system and contributed to the immediate flooding. The remainder was dealt with by natural storage on river flood plains, and to a lesser extent absorption and evaporation. The available area of natural storage of the river system amounted to approximately 10,000 acres (4,000 hectares), which included places like Anderson's Meadow (Figure 56). However the City Engineer noted how historical changes were continually reducing this available area, so that a subsequent similar flood would inevitably be more destructive in future if nothing else changed.

A decade further on, the report presented by the City Engineer in 1920 contained what must be the most authoritative map showing the lateral extent of the flooded areas in the city (Figure 57). He fully appreciated the significance of relative levels, and included a series of diagrammatic sections showing flood levels, normal tide levels and river bed levels, and how they varied along the length of the river. He also calculated the average river gradients through the city centre (see Appendix 5).

Some correspondents to the local press claimed that a high tide at Great Yarmouth had been a significant factor in 1912 in preventing the Yare water from 'getting away'.[7] This argument was refuted by the City Engineer, who was adamant that the tide level there was in fact low at the time of the flood, although he accepted that the increased silting that had occurred in Breydon Water and the flood sluices that had recently been installed at Oulton might have been contributory factors.

---

7 This was reported in the *Evening News* and *Eastern Daily Press* in January and February 1922.

Flood levels across the city

As part of this project, each of the Wensum flood markers that were found (15 in all) was surveyed to determine the flood level it records in terms of metres AOD, using nearby OS bench marks (see Appendix 2).

These measurements prove that the flood level was far from the same through the city centre, falling from over +4.1 m AOD above New Mills to +2.4 m AOD at Carrow. For comparison, the normal river levels are around +2.5 m AOD upstream of New Mills, and typically between about +0.6 m and +1.1 m AOD (varying tidally) at Carrow.

Farther upstream from the city centre, the recorded flood level was as high as +5.3 m AOD at Hellesdon Bridge, +5.1 m AOD at Norwich Waterworks and +4.9 m AOD inside St Barnabas Church. Downstream from Carrow, where the valley widens out and a large flood plain is available, a relatively unimpressive flood level of +1.9 m AOD is recorded on a marker plate on the Water's Edge Public House at Bramerton[8] (see Appendix 1).

On a smaller scale, it is interesting to note differences in the recorded floodwater level between the upstream and downstream sides of those four city bridges that have

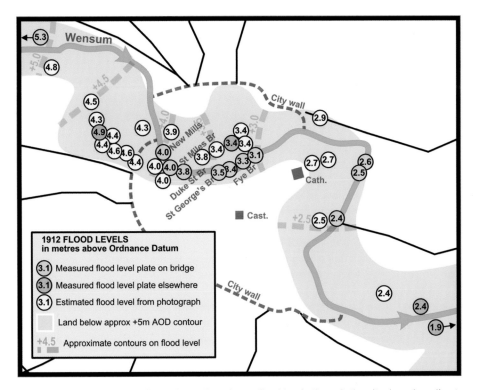

Figure 58 Sketch map showing estimated maximum flood levels through the city, based on direct measurement of surviving flood plates (see Appendix 2) and indirect estimation of flood levels from contemporary photographs (see Appendix 3)

8 It was formerly known as Bramerton Wood's End.

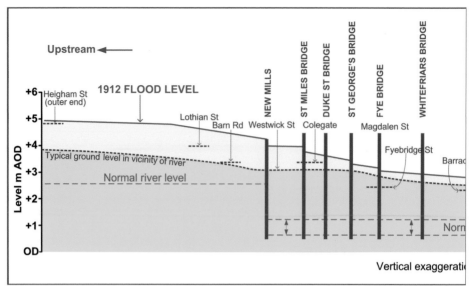

Figure 59 Schematic section along the River Wensum through the city centre showing 1912 flood

flood plates showing on both faces. The higher level is always recorded on the upstream side, and the difference varies from 7 cm at St George's Bridge to 19 cm at Fye Bridge. It should be borne in mind that Fye Bridge in particular was crossing a narrower and more constricted river in 1912 than we have today.[9] In a lecture delivered by the deputy City Engineer Harold Collins to Norwich Science Gossip Club in January 1913, he stated that the constriction of the six bridges from St Miles to Bishop Bridge caused a total 'heading up' of the flood of 2 ft 2 in (0.66 m).

Adding to these accurate measurements of flood marks, I have estimated water levels obtained from the inspection of photographs covering a further 22 locations. It has thus been possible to plot 1912 flood levels across most of the affected parts of the city, as shown in Figure 58. The calculated figures are presented to the nearest 0.1 m, but it should be noted that inherent approximations in the method mean there could be an error of perhaps 0.2–0.3 m in these estimated values.

Taken together, this comparative data quantifies the differences in floodwater level between the upstream and downstream sides of the city (see the long section in Figure 59), and this vertical difference in head amounted to around 2 m. It confirms that the heavy river flow was strongly constricted by the geometry of the upper part of the River Wensum at that time, particularly the degree of canalisation in the New Mills area and the presence of narrow bridges that partly dammed the flow.

This effect is most clearly demonstrated at St Miles Bridge at Bullard's Brewery, above which the river runs in an artificially narrow slot, and where the flood level was above the top of the arch of the bridge. As with other bridges, the flood level recorded on the upstream face of this bridge was higher than that on the downstream face, and the

---

9   This bridge was completely reconstructed with an extra arch in 1931–34.

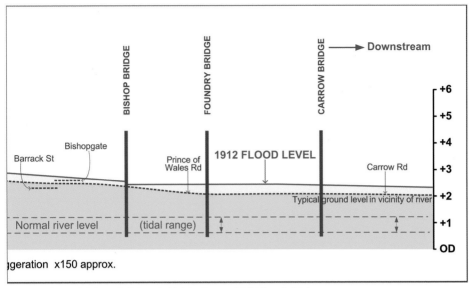

levels from Heigham (left-hand side) to Carrow (right-hand side)

damming effect of the 108-year-old structure is also clear from a photograph showing men rather inadvisably standing on it while water is squeezing through – this at a time when the structure must have under enormous lateral pressure from the weight of the water held back (Figure 60).

Water will find its way

The manner and route that the floodwater took as it moved through the city was the consequence of the interaction between the level of the water and the local topography.

In the upstream part of the city centre near Barn Road and Oak Street there is now no undeveloped low-lying flood plain left for the river to spill onto, since the original marshland was typically raised by filling to create a horizontal approach to the high river wall (see cross-section in Figure 6). Following the heavy rain in 1912, the already limited available flow space in the narrow river channel was additionally obstructed by floating debris from farther upstream, notably where the water was forced into narrow sluices at New Mills.

Given the exceptional volume of water trying to flow down the river, it is no surprise there was overspilling onto the adjacent flood plain areas upstream of the city centre in the Heigham and Hellesdon areas. This rose high enough to affect properties occupying the lower parts of the natural river terrace adjacent to the flood plain. This was the case along Heigham Street near the Dolphin Inn,[10] and at Russell Street, where flood levels of

---

10 Parts of Heigham Street were originally built as the Heigham Causeway along the edge of the natural flood plain, passing across a side tributary valley on the approximate line of Old Palace Road.

Figure 60 A man (said to be Harry Bullard's son Gerald) standing on St Miles Bridge looking downstream at the height of the flood. The water level is even higher than that in the back cover illustration of this book.

around +4.8 to +4.9 m AOD were recorded.

The evidence suggests that backing-up of water behind the artificial dam of New Mills, perhaps as far back as Heigham, was the single most important cause of the serious inundation of the low-lying residential streets off the north side of Dereham Road (Orchard Street and the surrounding area). This is the part of Norwich where the greatest floodwater depths were recorded, a consequence of the relatively small vertical difference between the normal river level and riverbank top level on the upstream side of New Mills. This is still the case today (see Figure 76). Contemporary photographs indicate waist-deep flooding in this area (see cover illustration), and the use of boats was necessary on several streets.

As well as overtopping New Mills, some of the flow which would normally have followed the meandering line of the river also seems to have taken a more direct course over the paved ground surface from the Heigham Street area to Westwick Street and St Margaret's Plain, then along the opposite side of the river via Colegate to Duke Street,[11] taking advantage of the blocked road gullies.

By the time the water had reached the southern part of Magdalen Street, the flood

---

11 In Duke Street and Colegate the road surface was entirely paved in wood blocks, which were lifted by floatation, adding to the debris (see Figure 46).

Figure 61 Extract from Morant's map of 1873 set as a perspective view upstream from New Mills, with the location of City Station superimposed in red

levels were at little more than 0.5 m above the typical ground surface in the area, which had historically been raised adjacent to the river. The circumstances were similar through the remainder of the low-lying parts if the city centre, where photographs certainly showed conditions to be difficult, but short of life-threatening.

Marginal low-lying properties in Barrack Street and those on Bishopgate were affected, but beyond Bishop Bridge the floodwater was merely spreading over the available flood plain areas, which were naturally there for that reason (see Figure 33). This included the built-up areas of Carrow, which in 1912 had only recently been reclaimed by development from natural grazing marshes.

The timing of the Great Flood

That this highest recorded flood occurred in the early twentieth century is significant. By 1912 there was the greatest extent of the river canalisation which had so accelerated during the industrial revolution.

It also postdated the construction of City Station (opened in 1882) which had involved deliberate reorganisation, narrowing and bridging of the previously braided river, as well as encroachment over the areas of flood plain farther upstream which had previously offered some flood protection to the city (Figure 61).

Additionally, there was the nearby Corporation Depot off Westwick Street which had been created by partial filling of the large mill pond upstream of New Mills. The bypass sluices had been retained but the channels formerly occupied by mill wheels were used for the turbines of the new sewage pumping station, built in 1897.

Recognising these cumulative physical effects of urban development, as the City Engineer did, helps to explain why this was such a high flood in comparison to what had happened previously after exceptional weather events.

Figure 62 1920s postcard view of Quayside before widening

9 Making space for water

River widening

The idea of deliberately increasing the river width was not new, but in previous centuries it was as much about space for river traffic as for the flow of water. For example, on 7 May 1825 a report in the *Norfolk Chronicle and Norwich Gazette* stated:

> It was proposed by the Common Council that a piece of ground adjoining the river, near St Michael's at Coslany Bridge, opposite Messrs. Harpers Dye Office, should be purchased at the price of £240 in order to increase the width of the river at this very narrow point, where it is only 26 feet wide, to 34 feet …

There had also been attempts (some perhaps misguided) to regulate the river, such as several similar schemes proposed in the 1830s to introduce lock gates between Pull's Ferry and Foundry Bridge (Figure 63).

As a direct result of the Great Flood of 1912, an initial scheme for river widening and improvement between New Mills and Foundry Bridge was approved by the City Council's Flood Prevention and Housing Committee in late 1914. The estimated cost was £142,000, and perhaps unsurprisingly in the wartime circumstances, the scheme failed to get the necessary Treasury approval four months later.

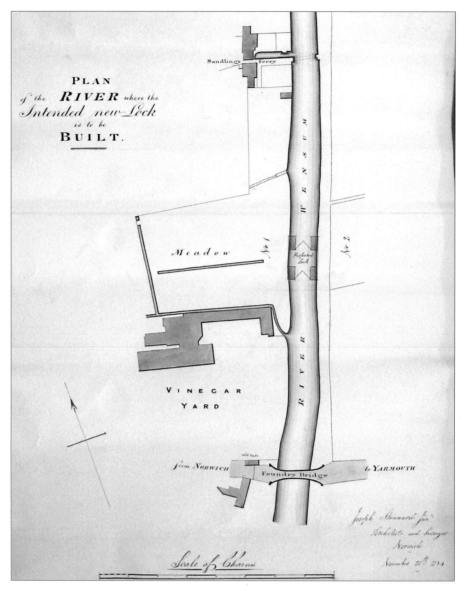

Figure 63 Joseph Stannard's 1834 plan for a lock gate between Pull's Ferry and Foundry Bridge

After the war a more comprehensive study was done, and the City Engineer (Figure 64) worked on another report.[1] Along the way, in 1919 he proposed the City should use its powers as river authority to prevent any more raising of river embankments in

---

1   His communications with committees were customarily signed off in an old-fashioned, somewhat obsequious style: 'I am, Gentlemen, your obedient servant ARTHUR E COLLINS, City Engineer.'

areas downstream, an area he described as a 'safety valve' (although preserving the flood plains upstream of the city was probably even more important). He argued that the safety of Norwich from floods depends on free dispersal of flood-water over the marshes below Norwich.

The report Arthur Collins presented to the committee in 1920 was written in the context of a city that was building for the future. Following the First World War, and before the full arrival of the Depression, there was a determination that this time there would be decisive action to deal with the future risk of flooding and ensure nothing like the Great Flood of 1912 ever happened again.

Figure 64 City Engineer Arthur E. Collins, pictured during the First World War, when he was Controller of Norwich Emergency Corps

The thrust of the City Engineer's recommendations was that the course of the river through the city centre should be enlarged, both to increase the amount of storage capacity in times of flood and to allow the water to get away more readily. He noted in the report that over the previous few centuries, the river banks had been encroached upon, leaving a river width varying between 25 and 95 ft (8–29 m) when it had once been 80 to 100 ft (24–30 m). Based on his estimate of a maximum flow capacity of 1,800 million gallons (8,200 million litres) of water in a single day, his calculations indicated the river channel needed to be 80 ft (24 m) wide to give reasonable protection against flooding.

River deepening

As well as setting back the river banks, the City Engineer recommended that the depth of the river should be maintained at 8 ft (2.4 m) below ordinary high water (OHWST[2]) down to Foundry Bridge, and 10 ft below OHWST downstream from Foundry Bridge. Ideally the dredge level would have been 10 ft over the full course of the river through the city, but this could only be considered once underpinning had been carried out to avoid undermining the existing bankside buildings. Alternatively, if they were to be removed as part of the river widening proposals, they would need to be demolished in advance of the dredging.

The City Engineer stated that with these measures there would still be slight flooding should an event of the magnitude of 1912 occur again, amounting to 9 in (20–25 cm) depth in places such as Bishopgate and Quayside.

---

2 Ordinary high water of spring tides, or about 3 ft (+0.91 m) AOD.

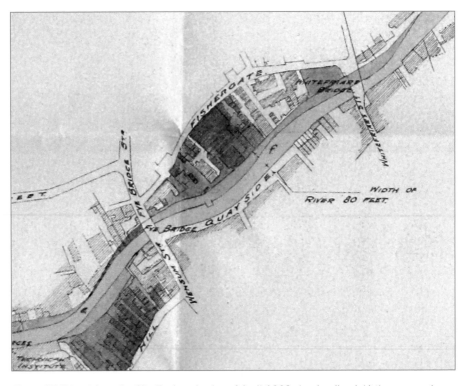

Figure 65 Extract from the City Engineer's plan of April 1928 showing (in pink) the proposed widening upstream and downstream from Fye Bridge (the full plan is in Appendix 5)

A major project

The report went on to list all the works that would be necessary, which included not only river widening but also the reconstruction of bridges, new embankments and dredging (Figure 65). It was an ambitious package of measures which would involve the acquisition of much existing property as well as major alterations or replacements of existing historic bridges, plus the promotion in Parliament of a bill to make it legally possible and to allow the finance to be raised.

It is not a surprise that it was not until 1929 that an updated report came back to the committee (now the Housing and Flood Prevention Committee) after a decade of further work including inspections and acquisitions.[3] The whole scheme was now costed at £371,000 (1929 figures), which excluded the enlargement of Duke's Palace Bridge (see Figure 66) and Bishop Bridge, two major elements it had reluctantly been decided to postpone. Whitefriars Bridge (Figure 67) had also in the meantime (1925) already been rebuilt in concrete, more than doubling its original span, as part of a much-needed job

---

3 This second report was written by Arthur Collins's successor, J. S. Bullough, who took over as City Engineer in 1925.

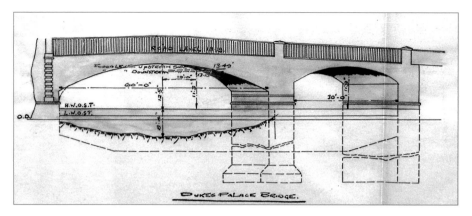

Figure 66 Extract from the City Engineer's drawing of April 1920 showing the proposed reconstruction of Duke's Palace Bridge (the full drawing is reproduced in Appendix 4)

Figure 67 The original Whitefriars Bridge before it was widened in 1924

creation scheme at the depth of the economic slump.[4] By the late 1920s the cost justification process was taking into account both the improvement in traffic conditions (from road-widening opportunities on reconstructed bridges) and the removal of substandard housing, in addition to the original core objective of prevention of flooding.

4 This project had been pushed through in the face of opposition from the newly formed Norwich Society, which did however succeed in saving Bishop Bridge.

Figure 68 Widening of the river downstream of Fye Bridge using a traction engine and dragline in 1934. The white building fronts onto Fishergate.

Figure 69 The reconstruction of Fye Bridge in 1933 in the distance, viewed from Crown Court Yard, Elm Hill, with the new river walls in place after widening

Figure 70 The narrow river downstream from St George's Bridge (to the rear of Elm Hill) before widening

What followed during the 1930s were major works to reconstruct Fye Bridge to make it both wider and longer (adding an extra arch), together with the necessary building demolitions, drag-lining and bank reconstruction. That succeeded in widening the river to the required 80 ft (24 m) in stages both upstream and downstream of Fye Bridge (Figure 68). These works are visible today as the concrete river walls between the upstream side of St George's Bridge and Whitefriars Bridge (Figure 69, which can be compared with Figure 70).

With the subsequent intervention of the Second World War and other reconstruction priorities rolled up into the 1945 *City of Norwich Plan*, the original far-sighted flood

Figure 71 An infill section of river wall being installed at the rear of Duke's Palace Wharf in November 2002, viewed from St George's Bridge

prevention scheme was never fully completed. This is the reason we still have some older bridges (notably St Miles Bridge, St George's Bridge and Bishop Bridge) surviving more or less in their original admired form, but all with the continuing potential to act as pinch points at a time of flood.

When considering the river geometry as a cause of flooding, the most critical section has arguably always been the strongly canalised stretch extending for about 500 m downstream from New Mills. In 1912 this part was closely flanked by industrial and warehouse buildings for virtually the whole way (see the back cover illustration). While most of those buildings have gone today, and there was a plan for extensive trimming back of the north bank, about three-quarters of those original river frontages remain in much the same position.

An extra sluice was added to the north side of New Mills and the bank trimmed back there in the 1930s, but the only other significant stretch widened was between St Miles Bridge and Duke's Palace Bridge, which was set back on the north side when the latter bridge was replaced and the Barnard's Works site redeveloped for housing in the late 1970s.

When the site upstream of St Miles Bridge was developed a decade later, no widening was carried out, but space was instead found to provide a riverside walk between the housing and the river wall. Part of the river upstream of St George's Bridge was even narrowed slightly with a new section of sheet-piled wall when Duke's Palace Wharf flats were built in 2002, directly opposite where the river had been widened 80 years previously (Figure 71). About 60 per cent of this 500 m length of the river still remains much

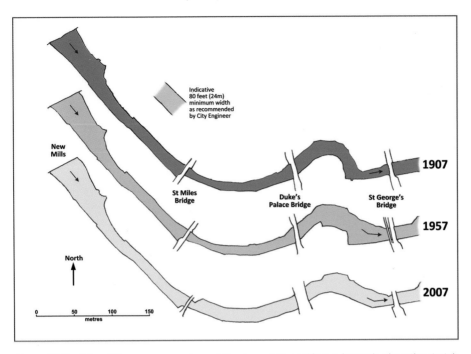

Figure 72 Spot the difference: comparison of the river width at 50-year intervals along the stretch downstream from New Mills. The necessary width recommended by the City Engineer is also indicated.

the same width as it was in 1912, and virtually none of the channel there is anything like the minimum width originally recommended by the City Engineer (see Figure 72).

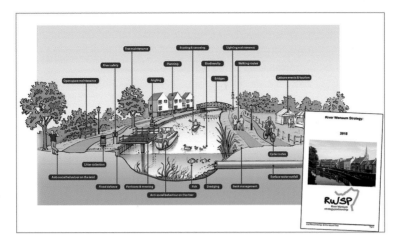

Figure 73 Diagram from the *River Wensum Strategy* document, published in 2018

10 And the future?

Long-term planning

Arthur Collins remarked in his 1920 report how serious floods in Norwich occurred at intervals of approximately one-third of a century. Perhaps he was also hinting that councillors should consider investing in preventive action well within that sort of timescale, before the memory of the last flood faded and the motivation to do something was lost.

In the event, the City Council did undertake much work preparing a package of flood prevention measures, and indeed implemented some of these, in spite of all the other competing demands for its attention like public housing and traffic planning – some of which were assimilated into the planned river improvements. Having said that, the stretches of river tackled were less critical to the flood risk than the ones left undone.

As an editorial in the *Eastern Evening News* on 18 January 1922 had warned:

The work of river widening, which has already been carried out as opportunity offers, must be carried on steadily to completion. It is one of those things in which success depends upon completion. To do it partially, and to leave river constrictions remaining here and there between the widened reaches of the river, would be to render the work partially done in a large measure futile.

By the time a third of a century had elapsed after 1912, a second major war had come along, bringing much urban devastation of its own. During the long recovery into the second half of the twentieth century much of the original momentum for flood prevention seems to have been lost.

The *City of Norwich Plan* of 1945 was largely focused on transport and public amenity issues, and the word 'flood' does not even appear in its index,[1] but it does state that 'Norwich has turned her back on the Wensum, while industry has helped itself.' Only 25 years later the river was no longer being used by any significant craft, industry was in strong decline and the Wensum gave rise only to intermittent complaints about the lack of dredging. Had we arrived at a situation of out of sight, out of mind?

As it happened, the end of the millennium was reached without any repeat of flooding of the 1912 severity. We might well ask whether this was merely good fortune, a sign that the partial river widening was successful, or down to some other explanation. I look at some of the factors involved in the following section.

Twenty years further on, and the *River Wensum Strategy* was published (in 2018) by a partnership of public bodies determined to realise the manifold benefits to the city of deliberate improvements to the river corridor. Most of the specific proposals in it are to do with access, leisure and environment, but it also expresses a desire to create additional floodwater storage along the river banks by naturalising the profile, and mentions New Mills as a possible location. Given the present strongly urban geometry and the likely limited funds available, it is difficult to see how such a policy could proceed beyond small-scale tokenism.

A changed scenario

Leaving aside the issue of partial river widening, it might be expected that much else has changed in the meantime that could affect the risk of fluvial flooding in Norwich since the City Engineer first presented his proposals nearly 100 years ago.

The city has greatly expanded, way beyond the extramural suburbs that existed in 1920. One consequence is the vastly increased extent of hard cover and the consequent increased risk and incidence of flash flooding (Figure 74). For a time during the late twentieth century the perceived solution was to improve storm water drainage systems, which sought to pipe the captured water as swiftly as possible to outfalls discharging directly into the river. Such a drainage solution would hardly have been helpful in a 1912 scenario; it would only have added to the flooding. Since then the engineering has become a little more enlightened, and there is now a preference for more sustainable drainage systems that hold back rainwater and where possible return it into the ground via soakaways and lagoons.

Coupled with the increasing demand for surface water drainage has been a large increase in water demand, from both population growth and increased per capita

---

1   In a section headed 'Barge traffic' the 1945 *Plan* does however make passing reference to river widening, 'particularly in the Coslany area, to a minimum of 80 feet as recommended in Reports submitted in the past'.

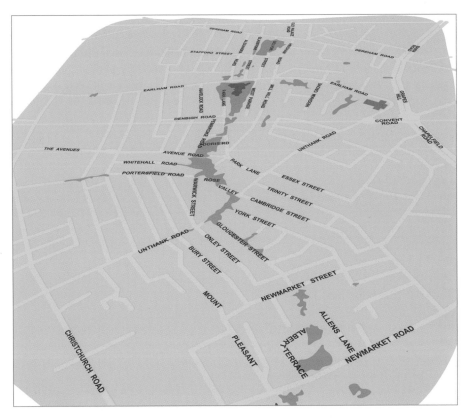

Figure 74 Sketch map showing the surface water flooding risk across the residential Golden Triangle part of the city (viewed northwards), interpreted from the County Council's surface water management plan. The blue and red represent flow and possible ponding, which is mostly along the line of a linear valley feature running between Newmarket Road and Old Palace Road.

consumption. The water abstracted from the River Wensum upstream of the city[2] is no longer sufficient to meet the demand, and the water supply is increasingly reliant on pumping from boreholes penetrating deep into the chalk substratum in locations outside the city. Two consequences of that trend are a potentially reduced natural recharge of the River Wensum in its upper reaches (perhaps lowering the river flow), and an increased volume of sewage to deal with at Whitlingham (downstream from the city) where the processed water is all discharged back into the river. The combined effect is a reduced river flow through the city centre (this has apparently been observed) compensated for by an increased flow farther downstream.

A further local complication is that the construction of a series of large-diameter sewers during the twentieth century (which involved further remodelling of parts of the river in places) has almost certainly modified some of the previous subterranean drainage

2   Until the 1980s water was abstracted from a site in Waterworks Road; since then it has come from Costessey.

conditions, as has the decommissioning of the numerous industrial abstraction wells that used to operate in the city centre.

Although the river has long been flanked by hard banks throughout its course in the city centre, the trend of bank raising (and building over flood plains) has continued in the more rural areas upstream and especially downstream. The latter could help to explain what may be a generally increasing tidal range over the years: the coastal fluctuation in water level that previously dissipated on its way from the sea is increasingly felt as far upriver as Norwich.

These days, most of the effort is put into planning for likely floods rather than trying to prevent them. New city centre homes have for some time been required to be constructed with built-in resilience. The measures include minimum floor levels above a defined flood level,[3] and low-lying areas generally used for car parking. However, there remain many older buildings with lower-lying floors or cellars (including of course numerous medieval churches) which remain as vulnerable as ever. While some localities could in theory be protected by flood banks or barriers, it is rarely practical to provide comprehensive protection in the built-up area.

Back to the weather

The big and uncertain environmental factor, which is the subject of constant debate these days, is of course climate change. A relevant question here is whether instability in the global weather systems is causing, or will lead to, a greater risk of extreme weather events of the type that led to the 1912 flood.

Certainly we have seen that freak rainfall events can take place against a general background trend of reducing average precipitation, in a similar way that the 1912 flood was caused by an exceptionally heavy rain event that took place during the summer, when general rainfall might have been expected to be relatively low (Figure 75).

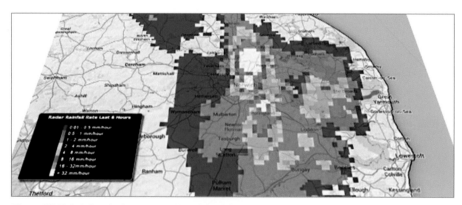

Figure 75 Rainfall radar image over Norwich at 3 pm on Sunday 20 July 2014. The white area indicates rainfall rates of more than 32 mm in an hour

---

3   The level used is based on advice from the Environment Agency, which is working on a new national flood risk management strategy (from 2019).

Figure 76 View across River Wensum and Barn Road 50 m upstream of New Mills, showing the limited clearance (freeboard) between the river level and the bank top

There is also the question of progressive sea level rise, which will increasingly affect base drainage levels in the tidal part of the river (that is, the lowest level to which water can drain by gravity). A high base level could be a factor that by chance coincided with an extreme weather event.

These are complex factors which are increasingly having to be taken into account when flood modelling is carried out, and are the basis for advice given by the Environment Agency and the planning requirements of the City Council.

The next Great Flood

Whatever the quantifiable risks of another storm of comparable magnitude, certain physical aspects of the river in Norwich remain closely similar to those that existed in 1912. One is the rather limited clearance between the normal river level and the bank top in the stretch above New Mills (see Figure 76), and another is the strongly canalised length of river downstream of New Mills at least as far as Duke Street Bridge.

It is difficult to avoid the conclusion that both of these factors mean that this part of the city will remain vulnerable to overspilling in circumstances of greatly increased river flow. The risks are not helped by the apparent lack of regular dredging, which would otherwise be a relatively simple way of providing more capacity.

While there are continuously monitored automated control sluices at New Mills (see Figure 12) and at other mills on the Wensum further upstream, it is hard to see that this control arrangement would be able to respond to a similar volume of flow as occurred in the 1912 event without comparable consequences,[4] which would also include the overloading of most the city centre's sewers.

So the past century has seen a change from active policies of flood prevention towards

---

4   In theory, this risk could be partly mitigated if it were possible to mobilise powerful temporary pumps during a flood crisis to move very large volumes of water directly from New Mills to below St George's Bridge.

reliance on passive flood management. There has been no recent serious fluvial flooding event in central Norwich to concentrate the mind. Most current attention seems to be focused on the issue of flash flooding rather than those areas vulnerable to fluvial flooding. We could ask whether there is a danger of a certain complacency setting in, and whether it will come back to bite us.

A similar question must have been on the mind of the writer of that same *Eastern Evening News* editorial of almost a century ago, only two years after the end of hostilities, who placed the risk of flooding alongside the geopolitical risk of war:

> Norwich has been periodically subject to disastrous floods, just as Europe has been periodically subject to disastrous wars. If the intervals between had been devoted to a removal of the causes, the circle of perpetual recurrence might have been broken and the city rendered safe. Unless the causes are effectively removed, another flood will follow that of 1912 just as certainly as the 1912 flood followed those which came before it.

However ominous those words seem in the light of what followed in 1939, hindsight and events often teach us that things can be more complicated than we think.

Could we one day see another flood approaching the magnitude of 1912's? Might there even be an event big enough to become the new Great Flood? Only time will tell.

Figure 77 A still from an animated film imagining a future Norwich flood

Appendix 1: Surviving 1912 flood plates

1 Hellesdon Bridge

2 Inside St Barnabas Church,
Russell Street

3 Pumping station,
New Mills Yard

4 St Miles Bridge (upper
side), Coslany Street

5 St Miles Bridge (lower
side), Coslany Street

6 St George's Bridge
(upper side)

7 St George's Bridge (lower side)

8 Off Colegate (No. 20)

9 Fye Bridge (upper side)

10 Fye Bridge (lower side)

11 Bishop Bridge (upper side)

12 Bishop Bridge (lower side)

13 Foundry Bridge (upper side)

14 Laurence Scott, Hardy Road

15 Water's Edge PH, Bramerton

Appendix 2: Measured levels on flood plates

Levels in metres AOD (above Ordinance Datum), as measured in December 2016 by surveying to nearby Ordnance Survey bench marks.

Hellesdon Bridge	+ 5.27
St Barnabas Church, Russell Street	+ 4.89
New Mills Yard	+ 4.01
St Miles Bridge upstream side	+ 3.96
St Miles Bridge downstream side	+ 3.79
St George's Bridge upstream side	+ 3.50
St George's Bridge downstream side	+ 3.43
No. 20 Colegate	+ 3.38
Fye Bridge upstream side	+ 3.28
Fye Bridge downstream side	+ 3.09
Bishop Bridge upstream side	+ 2.62
Bishop Bridge downstream side	+ 2.51
Foundry Bridge upstream side	+ 2.44
Laurence Scott	+ 2.43
Bramerton Woods End ('Water's Edge')	+ 1.86

Appendix 3: Estimated 1912 flood levels from contemporary photographs

Approximate levels in metres AOD (above Ordinance Datum), based on visual estimation of water depth and Ordnance Survey spot levels shown on contemporary or later 25 inch maps.

Heigham Street (Dial Square)	+ 4.8
Orchard Street	+ 4.6
Raglan Street	+ 4.6
Lothian Street	+ 4.6
Heigham Street (Barker Street)	+ 4.5
Mancroft Street	+ 4.4
Midland Street	+ 4.4
Barn Road	+ 4.4
Devonshire Street	+ 4.3
City Station	+ 4.3
St Margaret's Plain	+ 4.0
Coslany Street/Westwick Street	+ 4.0
Oak Street	+ 3.9
Duke Street	+ 3.8
St George's Street	+ 3.4
Fye Bridge Street	+ 3.4
Magdalen Street	+ 3.4
Barrack Street	+ 2.9
Bishopgate	+ 2.7
Great Hospital	+ 2.7
Prince of Wales Road/Rose Lane	+ 2.5
Carrow Road	+ 2.4

Appendix 4: 1912 flood levels recorded on a 1920 City Engineer's drawing

Levels recorded in decimal feet above original OD, as found noted on drawings accompany the City Engineer's report to the Flood Prevention Committee in 1920, with conversion to modern levels in brackets.

	Ft (decimal)	metres (AOD)
New Mills upstream side	16.73	(+ 4.70)
New Mills downstream side	14.60	(+ 4.05)
St Miles Bridge upstream side	14.22	(+ 3.93)
St Miles Bridge downstream side	13.59	(+ 3.75)
Duke's Palace Bridge upstream side	13.49	(+ 3.72)
Duke's Palace Bridge downstream side	13.10	(+ 3.60)
St George's Bridge upstream side	12.97	(+ 3.56)
St George's Bridge downstream side	12.73	(+ 3.48)
Fye Bridge upstream side	11.99	(+ 3.26)
Fye Bridge downstream side	11.76	(+ 3.19)
Whitefriars Bridge upstream side	11.04	(+ 2.97)
Whitefriars Bridge downstream side	10.71	(+ 2.87)
Bishop Bridge upstream side	9.99	(+ 2.65)
Bishop Bridge downstream side	9.53	(+ 2.51)
Foundry Bridge upstream side	9.34	(+ 2.45)
Foundry Bridge downstream side	9.31	(+ 2.44)
Carrow Bridge (proposed site of)	9.13	(+ 2.39)

Note on metric conversion

These original figures in feet have been converted to modern levels (m AOD) by first subtracting 1.30 ft (assumed recalibration of OD levels in the 1920s) then multiplying by 0.3048 (ft to m conversion). This produces flood levels that are very similar to those recently measured for the surviving flood places as part of this study (see Appendix 2).

Appendix 5: A selection of the City Engineer's plans and sections

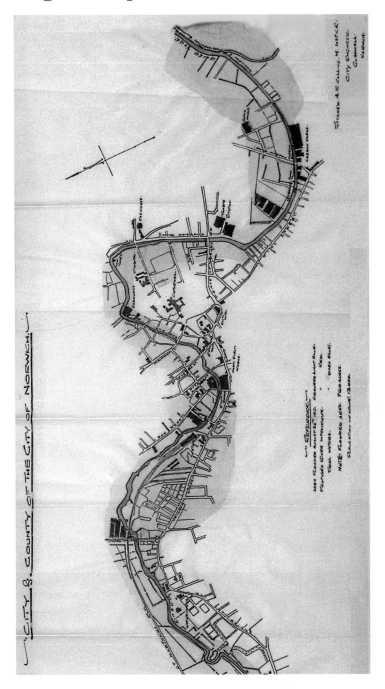

1920 map (traced in 1935) showing extent of flooding

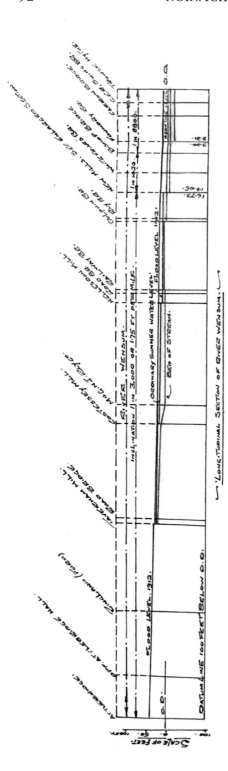

1920 longitudinal section along the River Wensum

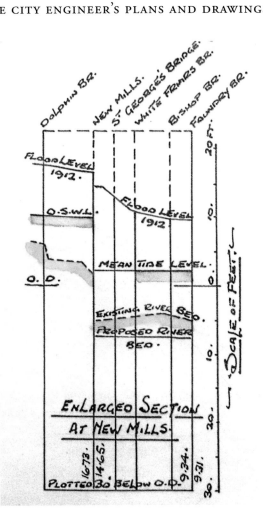

1920 diagram (extracted from a larger drawing) showing
relative levels of the River Wensum through the city

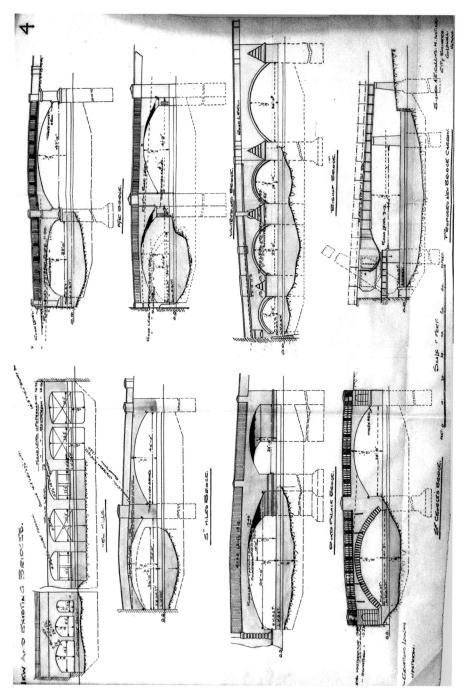

1920 drawing (traced in 1935) showing proposed bridge modifications

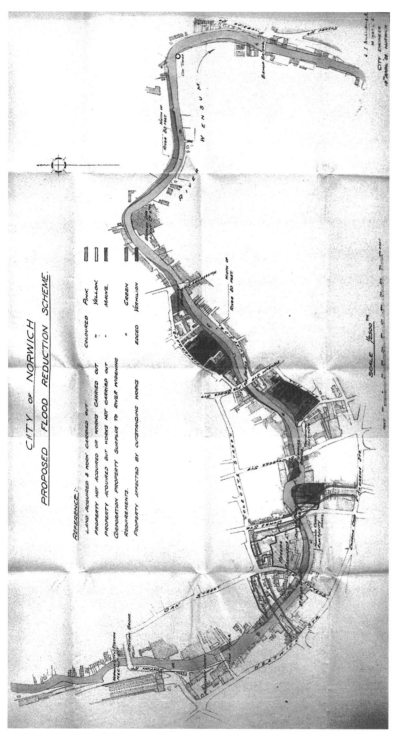

1928 plan showing progress of river widening and other improvements (key explains colours)

1930s plan showing progress of river widening and other improvements (completed in pink, proposed in yellow)

Appendix 6: Sketch plan showing locations of photographic and other figures

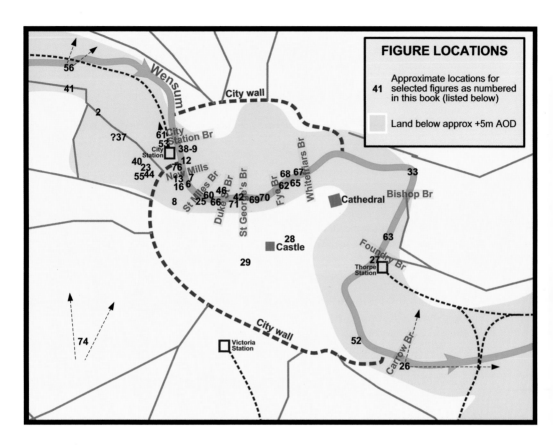

Locations included on the map above are for the following figures: 2, 6, 7, 8, 12, 13, 16, 23, 25, 26, 27, 28, 29, 33, 37, 38, 39, 40, 41, 42, 44, 46, 52, 53, 55, 56, 60, 61, 62, 63, 65, 66, 67, 68, 69, 70, 71, 74, 76.

References and further reading

1 Introduction

City of Norwich. 1912. *Illustrated Record of the Great Flood of August 1912.* Roberts & Co.

A. E. Coe & Son. 1912. *Photographs of the Floods in Norwich and Norfolk.* Book published in aid of the Lord Mayor's Relief Fund.

Bob Ogley, Mark Davison and Ian Currie. 1993. *The Norfolk and Suffolk Weather Book.* Froglets.

River Wensum Strategic Partnership. 2018. *River Wensum Strategy.* Norwich City Council.

William Smith. Undated. Untitled work on Norfolk. Oxford University Museum of Natural History Archives and Library Collection WS/F/4/3/001.

Neil R. Storey. 2012. *Norfolk Floods.* Halsgrove.

Matthew Williams. 2017. *Subterranean Norwich: the grain of the city.* Lasse Press.

2 The meandering river

Real time river levels can be viewed on the website: www.riverlevels.uk

Norfolk Mills website: www.norfolkmills.co.uk

3 A detective story

British Film Institute website: www.bfi.org.uk

Picture Norfolk website: www.norfolk.gov.uk/libraries-local-history-and-archives/photo-collections/picture-norfolk

George Plunkett website: www.georgeplunkett.co.uk

Tide levels information on website: www.broads-authority.gov.uk

Horace B. Woodward. 1881. *The Geology of the Country around Norwich.* Memoirs of the Geological Survey, HMSO.

4 The dress rehearsal

Newspapers available on microfiche at Norfolk Heritage Centre, Second floor, Norfolk and Norwich Millennium Library

5 Norwich in 1912

Newspapers available on microfiche at Norfolk Heritage Centre, Second floor, Norfolk and Norwich Millennium Library

6 A storm breaks

Mike Kendon and John Prior. 2011. 'Two remarkable British summers – 'perfect' 1911 and 'calamitous' 1912.' *Weather,* Vol. 66, No.7, Royal Meteorological Society/ *Quarterly Journal of the Royal Meteorological Society.* 1912. 'Unprecedented rainfall in East Anglia, August 25-26, 1912.' No. 165, Vol. 39.

Symons's Meteorological Magazine. 1912. 'Unprecedented rainfall in Norfolk.' No. 560, Vol. 47.

7 Politics, posing and the public good

George H. Fisher. 1913. *Fisher's Almanac*, published by bookseller and stationer of 105 Dereham Road.
Derek James. 2012, 2017. Various supplements in the *Evening News* featuring 1878 and 1912 floods. Archant.
Medical Officer of Health. 1913. 'Some features of the Norwich flood.' *Public Health*, Vol. 26, pp. 162–4.
Frank Meeres. 1998. *A History of Norwich*. Phillimore.
Maurice Morson. 2000. *A Force Remembered*. Breedon.
Norwich City Council. 1912. Town Clerk's scrapbook on the 1912 flood. Norfolk Record Office NCR 4g/10.
Norwich City Council. 1913. *Interim and Final Report on the Proceedings taken by and under the direction of Norwich Flood Relief Committee appointed by the Council on 28th August 1912, signed off by Henry J Copeman, Chairman.*

8 Understanding how it happened

Arthur E. Collins. 1919. *Report of the City Engineer to the General Purposes Committee with respect to River Widening*. Norfolk Record Office, N/TC 52/17.
Harold Collins. 1913. 'The Norwich flood', paper read to Norwich Science Gossip Club, published in *Proceedings 1912–13*. Norfolk Record Office, NCR 4g/10.

9 Making space for water

J. S. Bullough (City Engineer). 1929. *Report of the Housing and Flood Prevention Committee to the General Purposes Committee on works of River Widening*. Norfolk Record Office, N/TC 52/17.
Arthur E. Collins. 1919. *Report of the City Engineer to the General Purposes Committee with respect to River Widening*. Norfolk Record Office, N/TC 52/17.
C. H. James, S. Rowland Pierce and H. C. Rowley. 1945. *City of Norwich Plan*. City of Norwich Corporation.
Joseph Stannard Jr. 1830s. Lock on River Wensum at Thorpe Hamlet, plan in Norfolk Record Office, C/Scf 1/446.

10 And the future?

JBA Consulting. 2017. Greater Norwich Area Strategic Flood Risk Assessment. 2017, commissioned on behalf of a consortium of local authorities Norfolk County Council. 2011. *Norwich Surface Water Management Plan Final Report*. URS Scott Wilson.
River Wensum Strategic Partnership. 2018. *River Wensum Strategy*. Norwich City Council.
Environment Agency website:
www.gov.uk/government/organisations/environment-agency
Meteorological Office website: www.metoffice.gov.uk

Picture sources and credits

The author is most grateful to the organisations and individuals listed below for permission given to reproduce figures. Where not otherwise noted, photographs and drawings are by the author or reproduced from his own collection.

The author and publisher have made every effort to ensure that all necessary permissions have been obtained for the material reproduced. If however any omissions are brought to their attention, they will be happy to rectify them in future editions.

Figure 36 (Met Office plot of rainfall data in 1911 and 1912): reproduced from paper
Two remarkable British summers – 'perfect' 1911 and 'calamitous' 1912, Weather,
66: 179-184. doi:10.1002/wea.818 by Mike Kendon and John Prior, 2011, courtesy
of Met Office National Climate Information Centre https://www.metoffice.gov.uk/
climate.

Figure 37 (A family being rescued): courtesy of Archant/EDP library.

Figure 38 (Extract from Crome's painting): public domain image from Wikimedia
Commons.

Figure 41 (Milk delivery to Dial House): courtesy of Norfolk County Council Library
and Information Service. Enjoy thousands of images of Norfolk's unique history at
www.picture.norfolk.gov.uk.

Figure 42 (Photograph of the Norwich Mercury's damaged print works): from *Fisher's
Almanac 1913*, courtesy of Andrew Fisher.

Figure 43 (Notice in *Norwich Mercury* of 31 August 1912): courtesy of Norfolk
Heritage Centre, Norfolk County Council Library and Information Service.

Figure 44 (Posed picture of a food delivery at Lothian Street): courtesy of Broadland
Memories, website www.broadlandmemories.co.uk.

Figure 45 (Early poster issued on 29 August 1912): copied at Norfolk Record Office,
courtesy of Norfolk County Council Library and Information Service.

Figure 46 (Wooden paving blocks being collected from Duke Street): courtesy of
Norfolk County Council Library and Information Service. Enjoy thousands of
images of Norfolk's unique history at www.picture.norfolk.gov.uk.

Figures 47, 48, 49 (Two posters and a handwritten letter of thanks): courtesy of Norfolk
Record Office, Norfolk County Council Library and Information Service.

Figure 51 (Henry J Copeman, Lord Mayor of Norwich 1911-12): courtesy of Norfolk
County Council Library and Information Service. Enjoy thousands of images of
Norfolk's unique history at www.picture.norfolk.gov.uk.

Figure 52 (Aftermath of the flood at a house at King Street): courtesy of Norfolk
County Council Library and Information Service. Enjoy thousands of images of
Norfolk's unique history at www.picture.norfolk.gov.uk.

Figure 53 (City Station during the flood): courtesy of Norfolk County Council Library
and Information Service. Enjoy thousands of images of Norfolk's unique history at
www.picture.norfolk.gov.uk.

Figure 55 (photograph of flooded Lothian Street): from Philip Standley collection,
courtesy of Sarah Standley.

Figure 56 (Nineteenth-century photo of Anderson's Meadow): courtesy of Norfolk
County Council Library and Information Service. Enjoy thousands of images of
Norfolk's unique history at www.picture.norfolk.gov.uk.

Figure 57 (Extract from plan by City Engineer showing extent of 1912 flood): courtesy
of Norfolk Record Office, Norfolk County Council Library and Information Service.

Figure 60 (Man standing on St Miles Bridge during flood): courtesy of Norfolk County
Council Library and Information Service. Enjoy thousands of images of Norfolk's
unique history at www.picture.norfolk.gov.uk.

Figure 62 (1920s postcard view of Quayside before widening): from Philip Standley
collection, courtesy of Sarah Standley.

Figure 63 (Joseph Stannard's 1834 plan for a lock gate): courtesy of Norfolk Record Office, Norfolk County Council Library and Information Service.

Figure 64 (City Engineer Arthur E Collins): courtesy of Norfolk County Council Library and Information Service. Enjoy thousands of images of Norfolk's unique history at www.picture.norfolk.gov.uk.

Figures 65, 66 (Extracts from City Engineer's plan and drawing): courtesy of Norfolk Record Office, Norfolk County Council Library and Information Service.

Figure 67 (The original Whitefriars Bridge): courtesy of Norfolk County Council Library and Information Service. Enjoy thousands of images of Norfolk's unique history at www.picture.norfolk.gov.uk.

Figures 68, 69 (Widening of the river and reconstruction of Fye Bridge in 1933-34): from photographs by George Plunkett, courtesy of Jonathan Plunkett.

Figure 70 (The narrow river downstream from St George's Bridge): courtesy of Norfolk County Council Library and Information Service. Enjoy thousands of images of Norfolk's unique history at www.picture.norfolk.gov.uk.

Figure 73 (Diagram from published strategy document): reproduced from River Wensum Strategy, 2018, courtesy of River Wensum Strategy Partnership.

Figure 75 (Rainfall radar image over Norwich at 3pm on Sunday 20 July 2014): reproduced from obsolete Archant web article, courtesy of Met Office.

Figure 77 (A still from an animated film imagining a future Norwich flood): courtesy of an attender at the author's WEA Hidden Landscapes of Norwich course in 2014 (this kind person currently remains unidentified owing to the deletion of registers thanks to data protection rules).

Appendix 5: City Engineer's plans and drawings courtesy of Norfolk Record Office, Norfolk County Council Library and Information Service.

Index

The author

Matthew Williams graduated in geology and spent much of his career working in the construction industry, mostly in the East of England. His outside studies have extended into transportation and sustainability: he has developed a particular interest in the long-term development of urban areas, of which his home city of Norwich provides a key example. For the past ten years he has worked as a professional cycle instructor, maintaining a close physical connection with the city, and he has both spoken and published on the interwoven relationship between geology, place and history. His previous book, *Subterranean Norwich: The grain of the city,* was published by the Lasse Press in 2017.